An Introduction to 3D AutoCAD

A. Yarwood

G000060761

Longman Scientific & Technical

Copublished in the United States with
John Wiley & Sons, Inc., New York

Longman Scientific & Technical,
Longman Group UK Ltd,
Longman House, Burnt Mill, Harlow,
Essex CM20 2JE, England
and Associated Companies throughout the world.

Copublished in the United States with
John Wiley & Sons, Inc., 605 Third Avenue, New York, NY 10158

First published 1993

ISBN 0 582 209919
British Library Cataloguing in Publication Data
A CIP record for this book is available from the British Library

Library of Congress Cataloging in Publication Data
A CIP record for this book is available from the Library of Congress

Set by 8 in Melior 10/12 pt
Produced by Longman Singapore Publishers (Pte) Ltd.
Printed in Singapore

Contents

List of Plates (between pages 148 and 149)

Preface

Introduction

This book's contents are intended primarily for those using AutoCAD software with a PC (personal computer) working under MS-DOS. Its contents are however applicable to AutoCAD operating with other platforms.

The book has been written for students and other users of AutoCAD who are already reasonably conversant with AutoCAD for constructing two-dimensional (2D) drawings and who wish to understand the basics of creating three-dimensional (3D) models with the software. Although the book is based largely on the use of AutoCAD Release 11, much of its contents also apply to Release 10. Thus only the three Chapters 4, 5 and 6 are Release 11 specific, because they introduce the Tilemode system and the Advanced Modelling Extension (AME) software of Release 11. Other chapters in the book are pertinent to Releases 10 or 11. It is the Tilemode system of Release 11 which allows Release 10 drawing files to be loaded into Release 11. With the AME extension loaded into AutoCAD, 3D solid models can be created in Release 11. AME is an important development because it allows solid models to be created with a PC.

Chapters 8 and 9 describe elementary methods of producing renderings of 3D models in the two software packages AutoShade and Autodesk 3D Studio. Both Release 10 and Release 11 3D models can be rendered in either of these two packages. Autodesk 3D Studio is an excellent rendering software package, which should prove to be suitable for use by those wishing to produce good renderings of their 3D models.

Processor and memory requirements

While AutoCAD Release 10 can be loaded into a PC with the standard one megabyte of RAM (random access memory), containing 640 kilobytes of conventional memory and an 80286 CPU (central processing unit), Release 11 requires a minimum of an 80386 CPU and two megabytes of RAM.

It should be noted that Autodesk 3D Studio requires at least three megabytes of RAM.

AutoCAD Release 12

As this book was going into publication AutoCAD Release 12 had been announced. This important new release of the software, with its control systems in a windows type environment, does not introduce major changes in the way 3D models are created in AutoCAD. With this in mind, the contents of this book are as suitable for those working with Release 12 as those working with Release 11. Some notes on Release 12 are given in an appendix.

Earlier books by the same author

This is the third in a series of books designed for students wishing to learn how to use AutoCAD written by the same author. The earlier pair – *A Students AutoCAD* and *An AutoCAD Workbook* – have been received favourably. This third book has been written because, with the introduction of PCs with 32 bit systems, increased operating speeds and increased memory, users of AutoCAD are much more likely to need to study methods of creating 3D models with the aid of this CAD package. The rendering of 3D models with the aid of software such as Autodesk 3D Studio is also becoming into the range of students and others learning how to use CAD systems because of the rapid advances in PCs with 32 bit operating systems, increased speeds and memories.

Illustrations in the book

All illustrations in this book have been constructed with the aid of AutoCAD 386, working with an Epson AX3 (80386 CPU chip) computer, with 16 megabytes of extended/expanded memory. The line drawings were plotted on a Roland plotter.

Advantages of CAD drawing

Drawing with CAD software has one great advantage over drawing by hand. That is of being able to produce drawings much more quickly. A good rule to follow in order to make maximum use of the speed by which drawings can be produced with CAD software is:

Never draw the same thing twice.

This is because any drawing or part of a drawing can be arrayed, copied, dimensioned, inserted, moved, mirrored or rotated, without its having to be redrawn. Another speed of drawing factor is in the ability to add text in a variety of styles easily and quickly when working with CAD software such as AutoCAD. Note that AME models cannot be inserted into other drawings as blocks. If the attempt to insert an AME model is made, its handles are lost and, as a result, it is no longer a true AME model.

Acknowledgements

The author also wishes to acknowledge with grateful thanks the help given to him by members of the staff of Autodesk Ltd.

Registered trademarks

The following trademarks are registered in the US Patent and Trademark Office by Autodesk, Inc.:

Autodesk, AutoCAD, AutoShade, AutoSketch, Autodesk 3D Studio, Advanced Modelling Extension (AME).

IBM is a registered trademark of the International Business Machines Corporation.

MS-DOS is a registered trademark of the Microsoft Corporation.

A. Yarwood is a Registered Applications Developer with Autodesk Ltd.

CHAPTER 1

Introduction

The AutoCAD Main Menu and Drawing Editor screen

When AutoCAD is first loaded from disk, a **Main Menu** appears on screen (Fig. 1.1). In response to either Item 1 or Item 2 of this menu, the operator will *key* a suitable drawing file name and press *Return*. This brings the AutoCAD drawing editor on screen (Fig. 1.2).

```
              A U T O C A D (R)

Copyright (c) 1982—91  Autodesk, Inc.  All Rights Reserved.
Release 11ic2 (01/18/91) 386 DOS Extender
Serial Number: 000—123456

Current  drawing:


Main Menu
     0.  Exit AutoCAD
     1.  Begin a NEW drawing
     2.  Edit an EXISTING drawing
     3.  Plot a drawing
     4.  Printer Plot a drawing

     5.  Configure AutoCAD
     6.  File Utilities
     7.  Compile shape/font description file
     8.  Convert old drawing file
     9.  Recover damaged drawing

Enter selection:  1

Enter NAME of drawing:  draw\bracket
```

Fig. 1.1 The AutoCAD **Main Menu**

An AutoCAD workstation

Drawings produced with the aid of AutoCAD are usually constructed by a computer at a workstation. A simple workstation will consist of a computer with hard and floppy disk drives, connected to:

1. One or two *VDUs* (visual display unit), on the screens of which drawings and alphanumeric information will be displayed;
2. A pointing device – *puck, stylus, mouse, joystick* or *trackerball*

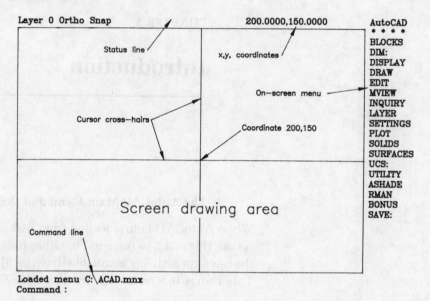

Fig. 1.2 The AutoCAD
drawing editor screen

— for controlling the position of a cursor on screen when
drawing, or for pointing to select commands or prompts from
menus which appear on screen;

3. A *graphics tablet* with an overlay on which commands and
prompts are printed (optional);

4. A *plotter* or *printer* for printing drawings on paper card or
tracing material — for producing *hardcopy*.

Methods of calling commands

In general AutoCAD provides four methods by which commands
can be called:

1. The name of the command may be *keyed* (or its abbreviation) at
the **Command:** prompt on the command line of the drawing
editor.

2. The command name may be pointed at and so *picked* from an
on-screen menu — usually on the right of the AutoCAD drawing
editor. The command name is repeated at the **Command:**
prompt on the command line — if the command name is
followed by a colon — e.g. **Line:**, an associated sub-menu
replaces the menu from which the command has been picked.

3. A menu name may be *picked* from the **Status** line of the
drawing editor. *Point* at the required menu name and the menu
is brought down on to the screen. The required command is

then *picked* from the pull-down menu. The command name, together with prompts, is then repeated at the command line.

4.   The required command name may be *picked* from a graphics tablet overlay connected to the computer.

When two VDUs are available at a workstation, drawings being constructed are displayed on one, while commands and associated prompts together with other alphanumeric information are displayed on the second.

Figure 1.3 shows the pull-down and the on-screen menus for the **CIRCLE** command.

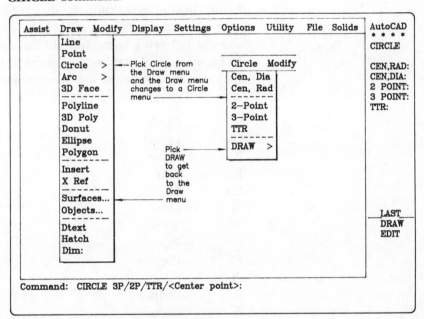

Fig. 1.3 The **Circle** menu from the **Draw** pull-down menu

Selection method used in this book

In this book it will be assumed that commands and their prompts are *keyed* at the keyboard of the computer using a single VDU set-up. In practice, the reader will use the methods best suited to his/her AutoCAD set-up – either keying commands, selecting them from an on-screen or from a pull-down menu or selection from a graphics tablet overlay. Some operators will prefer calling some commands from a graphics tablet overlay and *keying* responses for prompts – or other combinations of selection methods best suited to his/her own inclinations. However, one of the best and quickest ways for a beginner to learn the AutoCAD command systems is to start by typing all commands and responses into the command line of the drawing editor.

The file acad.pgp

As with other commands, those for constructing 3D drawings in AutoCAD can be called in several ways:

1. By *keying* in the commands at the keyboard;
2. By *selecting* the commands from relevant pull-down menus;
3. By *picking* the commands from relevant on-screen menus;
4. By *selecting* the command from a graphic tablet overlay.

Some commands can be *keyed* at the keyboard in the form of abbreviations. These depend upon the contents of the file *acad.pgp*, found in the *acad/support* directory. The standard file *acad/support/acad.pgp* from AutoCAD Release 11 allows an operator to use the following command abbreviations. The abbreviations can be keyed in either lower-case letters or in capitals. Those shown in italics in the list below are 3D commands:

A	Arc
C	Circle
DV	*Dview*
E	Erase
L	Line
LA	Layer
M	Move
MS	*MSpace*
P	Pan
PS	*PSpace*
PL	Pline
R	Redraw
Z	Zoom
B	Break
F	Fillet
TR	Trim
T	Text
S	Style
3DLINE	Line – hence L for *3Dline*
VP	*VPoint*
H	*Hide*

In addition the standard *acad/support/acad.pgp* file allows many abbreviations for commands in the Advanced Modelling Extension (AME) 3D modeling system. These will be discussed later (page 78).

Note that it is comparatively simple to amend the

acad/support/acad.pgp file to include any commands which an operator is using constantly, or to amend those already included in the file. Information describing such amendments are included in the file.

3D coordinates

All points on any drawing in AutoCAD can be defined in relation to x,y,z numbers in a three-dimensional coordinate system. They can be stated in figures – the distances in coordinate units from an origin defined as x,y,z = 0,0,0. Note that with two-dimensional (2D) drawings, the origin x,y coordinates are 0,0.

The origin (0,0,0) in AutoCAD is usually at the bottom left-hand corner of the drawing editor screen. However the origin may be altered, e.g. with the **Pan** command, or by changing its position when the User Coordinate System (UCS) is in operation (page 48).

The x and y axes are assumed to be lying horizontally and vertically on the screen surface, with the z axis lying perpendicular to the screen surface. With the origin (0,0,0) in its usual position, the directions of the x,y,z axes are as shown in Fig. 1.4. In relation to the screen surface:

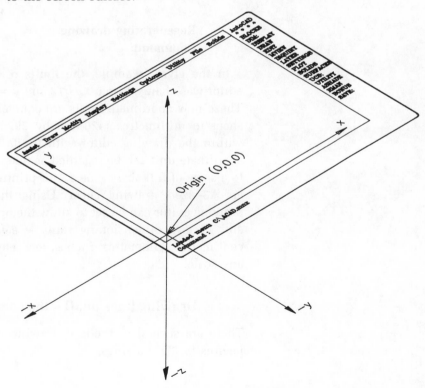

Fig. 1.4 The direction of the AutoCAD x, y and z axes

+ve   x is horizontally to the right of the origin;
−ve   x is horizontally to the left of the origin;
+ve   y is vertically above the origin;
−ve   y is vertically below the origin;
+ve   z is as if perpendicular and above the origin;
−ve   z is as if perpendicular and below the origin.

The number of coordinate units along each of the x, y and z axes available in the AutoCAD drawing editor is determined with the aid of the command **LIMITS**:

> **Command: LIMITS** *Return*
> **ON/OFF/<Lower left corner>: <0,0>:**   *Return*
> **Upper right corner <12,9>:** 420,297   *key Return*
> **Command:**

The screen will not be set fully to these limits until the command **ZOOM** is used to reset the screen to the stated coordinate limits as follows:

> **Command: z (ZOOM)**
> **ZOOM**
> **All/Center/Dynamic/Extents/Left/Previous/Vmax/Window/**
> $\qquad\qquad\qquad\qquad$ **<ScaleX/XP>:** a (All) *Return*
> **Regenerating drawing.**
> **Command:**

In the given example, the limits of the extent of the drawing editor was changed from x = 12 and y = 9 to x = 420 and y = 297. These new coordinate limits are equivalent to an A3 size drawing sheet in millimetres (420 mm by 297 mm). Thus when drawing within the drawing editor with limits set to x,y = 420,297 each coordinate unit can be regarded as one millimetre in order to draw to a scale of full size (scale 1:1) if printing and plotting full size on an A3-sized drawing sheet. Using the **LIMITS** command, the drawing editor can be set to allow the operator to draw to any scale and in any dimensioning units − e.g. to draw in millimetres, centimetres, kilometres, inches, feet, etc. on any size sheet and to any scale.

Drawing lines in 3D − the command LINE

There are several methods if drawing lines to defined coordinate lengths in 3D drawings.

By keying or picking absolute coordinate figures

When working with Release 11 of AutoCAD the command **LINE** can be called for drawing lines in 2D or 3D. Note that if working with Release 10, lines in 3D can only be drawn if the command **3DLINE** is called. **LINE** can be called by either keying *l* (Line) in response to the **Command:** prompt at the command line, by selecting **LINE:** from the **DRAW** on-screen menu, or by selecting **Line** from the **Draw** pull-down menu. With any one of these methods, the following appears at the command line of the drawing editor:

Command:
LINE from point: *key, Return or pick coordinate points*
To point: *key, Return or pick coordinate points*
To point:

In response to each of these prompts, the operator can key in the required coordinates. An example is given in Fig. 1.5.

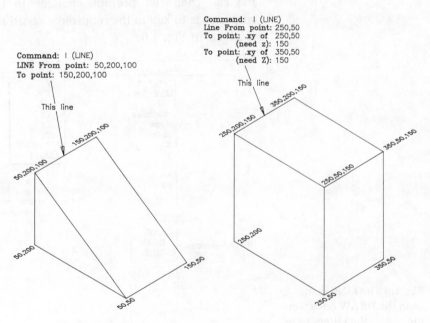

Fig. 1.5 The **LINE** command for drawing 3D lines

Command: l (LINE)   *key Return*
LINE from point: 50,50   *key Return*
To point: 50,200,100   *key Return*
To point: 150,200,100   *key Return*
To point: 150,50   *key Return*
To point: 50,50   *key Return*

To point: 50,200   *key Return*
To point: 50,200,100   *key Return*
To point: *Return*
Command:

By using filters

When **LINE** is selected from either an on-screen or a pull-down menu, the **LINE:** on-screen sub-menu appears in the on-screen menu area. This menu includes *filters*. Similar filters can be brought on screen by selecting the **Assist** pull-down menu, and *picking* **Filters>**. The **Filters** pull-down menu then replaces the **Assist** menu. Both these filter menus are shown in Fig. 1.6. The following example shows how filters are used. When **.xy** is *picked* from either of the filter menus **.xy of** appears as a prompt at the command line. This is followed by either keying the *x-,y-*coordinate numbers or *picking* a point on screen with the selection device. Then the prompt changes to **(need Z)**, to which the response is to key in the required *z* coordinate number. An example is given in Fig. 1.6:

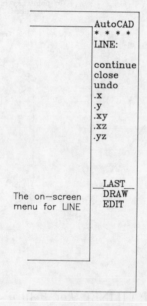

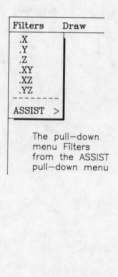

The pull-down
menu Filters
from the ASSIST
pull-down menu

The on-screen
menu for LINE

Fig. 1.6 The **LINE** menu from the **DRAW** on-screen menu and the **Filters** pull-down menu

Command:
LINE From point: 250,50   *key or pick with selection device*
To point: .xy of 250,50   *key or pick*
  (need Z): 150   *key Return*

> **To point: .xy of** 350,50   *key Return*
>   **(need Z):** 150   *key Return*
> **To point:** 350,50   *key Return*
> **To point:** 250,50   *key Return*
> **To point:** 250,200   *key Return*
> **To point: .xy of** 250,200   *key Return*
>   **(need Z):** 150   *key Return*
> **To point: .xy of** 350,200   *key Return*
>   **(need Z):** 150   *key Return*
> **To point: .xy of** 350,50   *key Return*
>   **(need Z):** 150   *key Return*
> **To point:**   *Return*
> **Command:**

With relative coordinates

Relative coordinates – those relative in position to the last stated coordinate – can be either *keyed* or partly picked and partly *keyed* either with or without the aid of filters.

Relative coordinates are in the form of the following examples:

@100,0,0 – a coordinate position 100 units along the x axis relative to the last given position;

@0,100,0 – a coordinate position 100 units along the y axis relative to the last given position;

@0,0,100 – a coordinate position 100 units along the z axis relative to the last given position;

@100<45 – a coordinate point 100 units distant from and at an angle of 45° to the last given point.

Two examples are given in Fig. 1.7. The figures keyed at the command line to obtain these examples are given below:

The left-hand figure

> **Command:** l (LINE) *key Return*
> **Line from point:** 70,80   *key Return*
> **To point:** @100,0,150   *key Return*
> **To point:** @0,0,100   *key Return*
> **To point:** @−100,0,0   *key Return*
> **To point:** @0,100,−50   *key Return*
> **To point:** c (close)   *key Return*
> **Command:**

Note: the use of negative coordinate numbers.

The right-hand figure

Line from point: 250,150   *Keyboard Return*
To point: @100<45   *key Return*
To point: @100<135   *key Return*
To point: @0,0,100   *key Return*
To point: @100<315   *key Return*
To point: @0,0,100   *key Return*
To point: @0,100,0   *key Return*
To point: c (close)   *key Return*
Command:

Note: the use of relative angular coordinate numbers (e.g. @100<45).

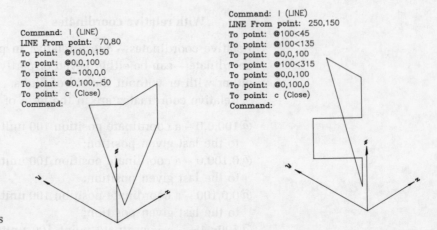

```
Command:  l (LINE)
LINE From point:  70,80
To point:  @100,0,150
To point:  @0,0,100
To point:  @-100,0,0
To point:  @0,100,-50
To point:  c (Close)
Command:
```

```
Command:  l (LINE)
LINE From point:  250,150
To point:  @100<45
To point:  @100<135
To point:  @0,0,100
To point:  @100<315
To point:  @0,0,100
To point:  @0,100,0
To point:  c (Close)
Command:
```

Fig. 1.7 Examples of 3D lines

The command 3DFACE

Many 3D drawings can be constructed entirely by using the **LINE** and the **3DFACE** commands. When constructed with 3Dfaces, the **HIDE** command will remove all hidden lines from behind the faces. 3Dfaces can be constructed as flat surfaces (planar) or as non-planar surfaces in 3D space. 3Dfaces are formed as triangles or as quadrilaterals – i.e. with three or four edges. There is more about **3DFACE** in Chapter 2. When **3DFACE** is called:

Command: 3dface   *key Return*
First point: coordinates   *key Return*
Second point: coordinates   *key Return*
Third point: coordinates   *key Return*
Fourth point: coordinates   *key Return*

Third point: *Return*
Command:

and a quadrilateral 3Dface is formed.

The command VPOINT

When a 3D drawing has been constructed in the WCS (World Coordinate System), the result will be a plan view – i.e. as seen from above, with the x–y plane flat on the screen surface. An example of such a plan view drawn with the aid of the command **3DFACE** is given in Fig. 1.8.

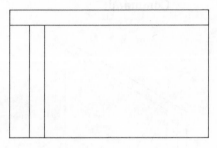

Plan view of 3D drawing in World Coordinate System

Fig. 1.8 Plan view of a 3D drawing in the World Coordinate System (WCS)

The **VPOINT** command system allows the determining of new viewing positions in 3D space from which the user will be able to see a pictorial view of a 3D drawing.

When **VPOINT** is called – abbreviation vp – and *Return* pressed, the command line shows:

Command: vp (VPOINT)   *Return*
VPOINT Rotate/<View point> <0,0,1>:

There are three ways of responding to these prompts:

Keying x,y,z coordinates

Command: vp (VPOINT)   *Return*
VPOINT Rotate/<View point> <0,0,1>: −1,−1,1   *Return*
Regenerating drawing.
Command:

This results in a pictorial parallel projection view of the 3D drawing appearing on screen as in Fig. 1.9. The *keyed* x,y,z coordinates determine the viewing position as seen looking towards the origin 0,0,0. Thus with x,y,z at −1,−1,1, the viewing is looking towards the origin from x = −1 (i.e. from the left), with y = −1 (i.e. from the front) and with z = 1 (i.e. from above). The view is therefore looking from the left front from above. Such coordinate figures used with **VPOINT** do not indicate any distance from the origin. The new view will appear occupying its full extents on screen. In order to bring the view back to its normal scale size, it is necessary to **ZOOM** the drawing to scale 1:1 by:

Command: z (ZOOM)   *Return*
All/Center/Dynamic/Extents/Left/Previous/Vmax/Window/
<Scale(X/XP)>: 1   *Return*

Regenerating drawing:
Command:

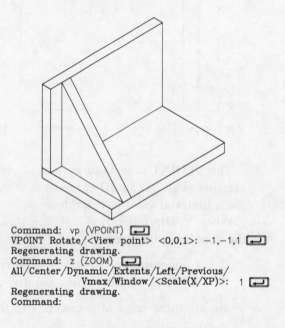

```
Command: vp (VPOINT) ⏎
VPOINT Rotate/<View point> <0,0,1>: −1,−1,1 ⏎
Regenerating drawing.
Command: z (ZOOM) ⏎
All/Center/Dynamic/Extents/Left/Previous/
        Vmax/Window/<Scale(X/XP)>:  1 ⏎
Regenerating drawing.
Command:
```

Fig. 1.9 The 3D model (Fig. 1.8) from view point −1,−1,1

Figure 1.10 shows the results of keying in a variety of x,y,z coordinate numbers in response to the **<View point>** prompt.

Keying r (Rotate)

This is followed by keying in two angles to obtain the required viewing position. The first is the angle made to the x axis in the x-y plane; the second is the angle made to the x-y plane:

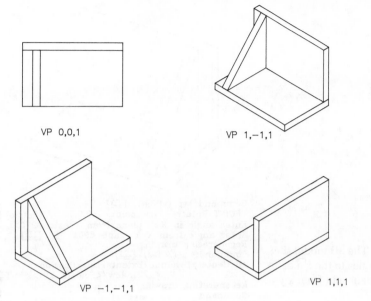

VP 0,0,1 VP 1,−1,1

Fig. 1.10 The 3D model (Fig. 1.8) from various view points

VP −1,−1,1 VP 1,1,1

Command: vp (VPOINT) *Return*
VPOINT Rotate/<View point> <0,0,1>: r (Rotate) *Return*
Enter angle in X-Y plane from X axis <270>: 240 *Return*
Enter angle from X-Y plane <90>: 30 *Return*
Regenerating drawing.
Command: z (ZOOM) *Return*
All/Center/Dynamic/Extents/Left/Previous/Vmax/Window/
                              <Scale(X/XP)>: 1 *Return*
Regenerating drawing:
Command:

The resulting pictorial view is shown in Fig. 1.11.

Pressing Return twice

The screen changes and two icons appear (the compass and axes tripod icons of **VPOINT**) as shown in Fig. 1.12. The first is a double circle with crossing vertical and horizontal lines. This represents a world view of the screen. In this globe view:

1.   The centre represents the north pole (0,0,1);
2.   The inner circle represents an equator (n,n,0);
3.   The outer circle represents the south pole (0,0,−1).

A tiny cursor cross, which can be manipulated by moving the pointing device, can be moved to any position on, around or in this world icon.

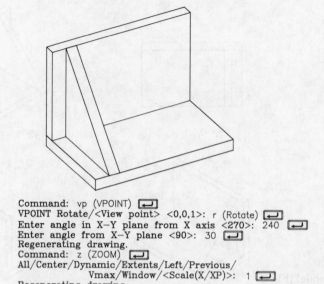

```
Command: vp (VPOINT) ⏎
VPOINT Rotate/<View point> <0,0,1>: r (Rotate) ⏎
Enter angle in X–Y plane from X axis <270>: 240 ⏎
Enter angle from X–Y plane <90>: 30 ⏎
Regenerating drawing.
Command: z (ZOOM) ⏎
All/Center/Dynamic/Extents/Left/Previous/
          Vmax/Window/<Scale(X/XP)>:  1 ⏎
Regenerating drawing.
Command:
```

Fig. 1.11 The 3D model (Fig. 1.8) at angles to the x axis in the x-y plane and from x-y plane

The second icon is a tripod showing the relative positions of the x, y and z axes as the cursor is moved around the world view icon.

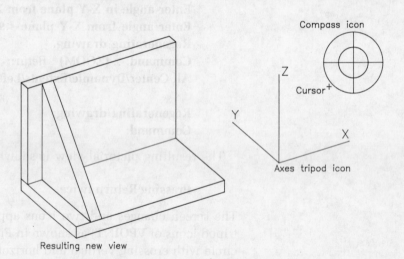

Fig. 1.12 The **VPOINT** compass and axes tripod display

Resulting new view

A required viewing position is determined by moving the cursor around the world icon with the aid of the selection device, noting the relative positions of the three coordinate axes, then pressing the *pick* button of the selection device when a required position has been selected. The screen then reverts to show a pictorial view of the 3D drawing as seen from the new selected viewing position.

Notes:

1. When working with AutoCAD Release 11, **VPOINT** is only effective when in Model space (MSPACE).
2. VPOINT can only be used in the current **VIEWPORT** (see page 66).
3. **VPOINT** pictorial views are in parallel projections – i.e. perspective is not applied.
4. The need to zoom the drawing to scale 1:1 after a new **VPOINT** has been chosen. This is because when a new **VPOINT** is called, the resulting new view on the screen is scaled to its current extents.
5. When deciding x,y,z coordinates for View points, the direction of viewing is always towards the origin (0,0,0). The distance of the View point from the origin is not included.

The command HIDE

If a 3D drawing has been constructed with the aid of any of the commands: **3Dface**, **EDGESURF**, **REVSURF**, **RULESURF**, **TAB-SURF**, or with **3DMESH** or **PFACE** (see Chapter 2), or if constructed as a 3D model with the aid of the Advanced Modeling Extension (AME) (see Chapter 5), then all hidden lines behind the surfaces or surface meshes of the drawing can be hidden by calling the command **HIDE**.

> **Command:** h (Hide)   *Return*
> **HIDE Regenerating drawing.**
> **Removing hidden lines: 775** (*in 25s depending upon complexity of the drawing*)
> **Command:**

Once *Return* has been pressed after calling the command, no further action is required. When the command is called, the drawing disappears from the screen. After all hidden lines have been removed, the 3D drawing with hidden lines removed reappears on screen. The process of hiding hidden lines can take a considerable time if a large number of lines have to be hidden.

The command ELEV

When this command is called, the command line shows:

> **Command:** elev   *key Return*
> **New current elevation <0>:**
> **New current thickness <0>:**

The current elevation is, initially, the position of the x,y plane with z at 0. If a new current elevation of say 50 is chosen, the x,y plane will then be positioned 50 coordinate units in the z direction above its original elevation. Figure 1.13 shows a screen view of a number of AutoCAD objects drawn in plan view (in the WCS).

The current thickness is the extrusion thickness for any 2D object which is drawn when an elevation thickness is current. Figure 1.14 shows how the various 2D objects of Fig. 1.13 are extruded with the current elevation at 0 and the current thickness at 50. The vertical faces of extruded 2D entities are 3D faces, but only in the case of extruded circles do the top faces of the extrusions become 3D faces. Thus when **HIDE** is called, the resulting hidden line views are as shown in Fig. 1.14.

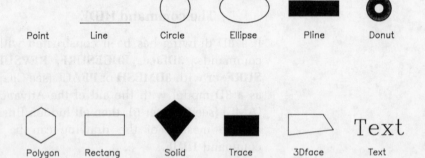

Fig. 1.13 Objects drawn in the WCS with the aid of **DRAW** commands at elevation 0 and thickness 50

The following features are ignored by the **ELEV**ation command: 3D faces, 3D polylines, 3D polygon meshes and dimensions. These features cannot be extruded by **ELEV**ation.

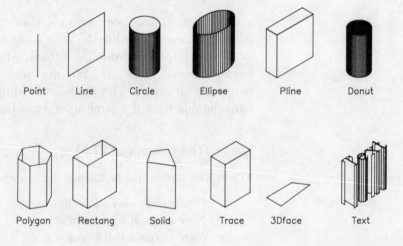

Fig. 1.14 **VPOINT** view of the objects in Fig. 1.13

Note that even if **SOLID FILL** is **ON**, when **VPOINT** is called to view extrusions in 3D, those areas which are solid filled in 2D are not solid filled in 3D.

It is particularly important to realise, when working in 3D in Model Space, that the setting of the current elevation will affect the positions of drawings relative to the initial setting of the x,y plane.

Figure 1.15 shows two plan views (in the WCS) of a 3D drawing constructed on three current elevation and thickness settings. The drawings therefore consist of three extrusions. The lower drawing of the two in Fig. 1.15 has had 3D faces added with **ELEV**ation set to two different current elevations but with the current thickness at 0 at each elevation.

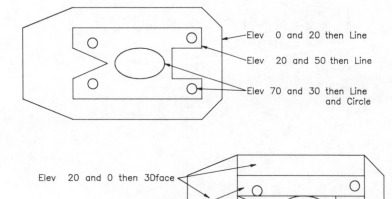

Fig. 1.15 A 3D model on different elevations and of differing thicknesses. The lower drawing has 3D faces added

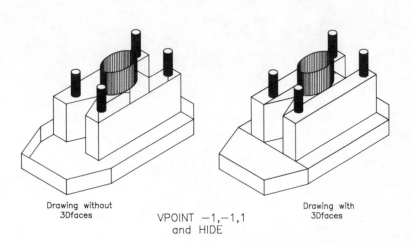

Fig. 1.16 **VPOINT** view of the 3D drawing Fig. 1.15

Figure 1.16 is a pictorial view of the two 3D drawings of Fig. 1.15 after calling **VPOINT** at −1,−1,1. **HIDE** has been called after **VPOINT** to hide hidden lines behind the 3D faces of the right-hand pictorial drawing.

CHAPTER 2

3D Drawing Commands from the SURFACES menu

Introduction

There are a number of command systems available in AutoCAD Release 11 for the construction of 3D drawings. In addition the User Coordinate System (UCS) allows 3D drawings to be constructed on coordinate systems of the operator's own choice. More about the UCS in Chapter 3. This chapter is devoted to the use of the commands **LINE**, **3DLINE** and the command systems from the **SURFACES** menus – either the **SURFACES** on-screen menu or the **SURFACES...** menu from the **DRAW** pull-down menu.

The commands 3DLINE and 3DFACE

The two commands most likely to be used in the construction of 3D drawings are **3DLINE** (**LINE**) and **3DFACE**. These have already been touched upon in Chapter 1. Further examples of constructions involving **3DFACE** will be given in this chapter. Two 3D drawings of a simple block, one drawn with **3DLINE** and the other with **3DFACE**, are compared in Fig. 2.1, which shows that hidden lines of drawings constructed with **3DLINE** cannot have hidden lines removed. Lines behind the surfaces of 3D drawings constructed with the aid of **3DFACE** can be removed by calling **HIDE**.

3DFACES are constructed as three-dimensional polygonal surface meshes. The meshes may be coplanar or nonplanar. Each 3D face is either a triangle or a quadrilateral. This means that complicated 3D surfaces can only be constructed as a series of adjoining triangles or quadrilaterals. The lines between adjacent triangles or quadrilaterals in surfaces constructed from a number of 3D faces can be removed by taking advantage of the invisible prompt of the **3DFACE** command system. Otherwise all edges of the triangles or quadrilaterals will appear in a 3D drawing constructed with the aid of **3DFACE**.

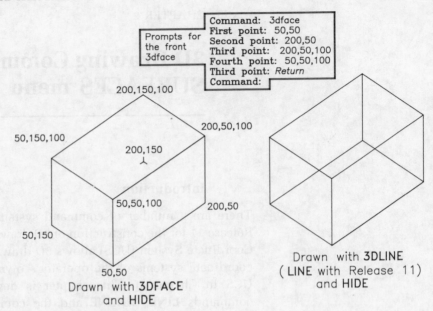

```
Command: 3dface
First point: 50,50
Second point: 200,50
Third point: 200,50,100
Fourth point: 50,50,100
Third point: Return
Command:
```

Prompts for the front 3dface

200,150,100

50,150,100   200,50,100

200,150
⊥

50,50,100   200,50

50,150

Drawn with 3DLINE
(LINE with Release 11)
and HIDE

50,50
Drawn with 3DFACE
and HIDE

Fig. 2.1 The command
3DFACE compared with
3DLINE

The SURFACE commands

When **SURFACES** is selected from the AutoCAD on-screen menu, a sub-menu showing the types of **SURFACE** meshes available appears in place of the AutoCAD menu – Fig. 2.2. Select **3DFACE** from this sub-menu and the **3DFACE** sub-menu appears in its place. Select **3DPOLY** from the sub-menu and the **3DPOLY** sub-menu takes its place. All three sub-menus are shown in Fig. 2.2. Examples of each of the Surface commands in the **SURFACES** menu are given in this chapter.

When **SURFACES. . .** is selected from the **DRAW** on-screen menu, the **3D Surface Commands** dialogue box appears (Fig. 2.3). As can be seen from this dialogue box, the same surface command systems can be called by *pointing* at the relevant square on the left of the chosen command in the dialogue box, as can be called from the **SURFACES** on-screen sub-menu. The 3D Objects choice shown in both the **SURFACES** on-screen menu and in the **3D Surface Commands** dialogue box will be described on page 43.

As with 3D faces, all 3D surfaces are composed of surface meshes made up of adjoining triangles or quadrilaterals. Lines behind these surface meshes can be removed by calling the command **HIDE**.

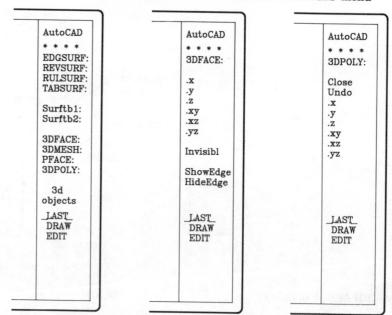

Fig. 2.2 The **SURFACES** on-screen menu with its sub-menus **3DFACE** and **3DPOLY**

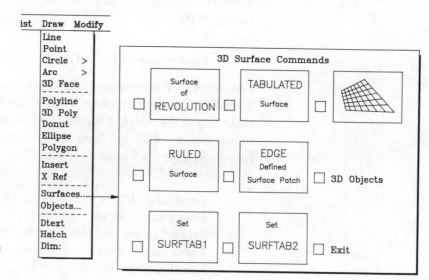

Fig. 2.3 The **Draw** pull-down menu and the **3D Surface Commands** dialogue box

The command 3DFACE

Three examples of simple drawings of blocks constructed with the aid of the command **3DFACE** are given in Figs. 2.4, 2.5 and 2.6. The reader is recommended to draw these three blocks from the instructions given below and in the illustrations. In each of the given examples, the 3D drawing have been viewed by calling

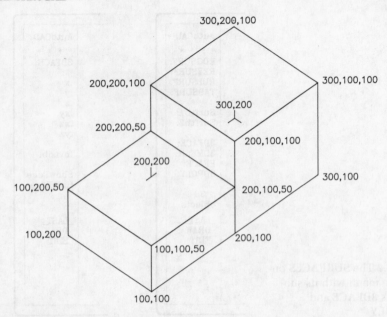

Fig. 2.4 **3DFACE** – Example 1

VPOINT, *keying* −1,−1,1 and then removing hidden edges by calling **HIDE**.

First example (Fig. 2.4)

Figure 2.4 is a 3D drawing of a block constructed with the aid of **3DFACE**. It is made up of 10 3D faces. No attempt has been made to make any of the edges of the 3D faces invisible. The 3D coordinates of the corners of all the faces are included in Fig. 2.4. Using only two-dimensional x,y coordinates the base of the block was drawn as follows:

> **Command:** 3dface   *key Return*
> **First point:** 100,100   *key Return*
> **Second point:** 300,100   *key Return*
> **Third point:** 300,200   *key Return*
> **Fourth point:** 100,200   *key Return*
> **Third point:**   *Return*
> **Command:**

Note the second appearance of **Third point:**, to which the response is to press the *Return* key if one wishes to complete a single 3D face. Continuing keying or selecting coordinates at the second appearance of **Third point:** is explained in Figs 2.8 and 2.9.

Using three-dimensional x,y,z coordinates, the uppermost face of the block was drawn as follows:

Command: 3dface   *key Return*
First point: 200,100,100   *key Return*
Second point: 300,100,100   *key Return*
Third point: 300,200,100   *key Return*
Fourth point: 200,200,100   *key Return*
Third point: *Return*
Command:

Second example (Fig. 2.5)

Figure 2.5 is a 3D drawing of a block, parts of which have been drawn by copying or mirroring faces already drawn, in order to speed up the construction. Those parts which were copied and mirrored are shown in Fig. 2.5.

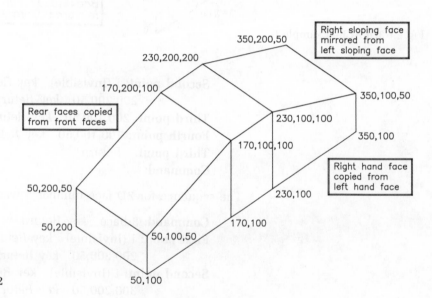

Fig. 2.5 **3DFACE** – Example 2

Third example (Fig. 2.6)

Another example where some 3D faces have been mirrored.

The command 3DFACE with the invisible prompt

Figure 2.7 is an example of a 3D surface constructed from five 3D faces, with some edges made invisible by involving the Invisible prompt. The sequence of constructing 3D face number 1 was:

Command: 3dface   *key Return*
First point: 100,200,50   *key Return*

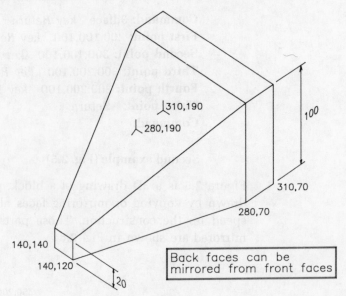

310,190

280,190

100

310,70

280,70

140,140

140,120

20

Back faces can be
mirrored from front faces

Fig. 2.6 **3DFACE** – Example 3

Second point: i (Invisible)   *key Return*
                200,200,50   *key Return*
Third point: 200,100,50   *key Return*
Fourth point: 100,100,50   *key Return*
Third point: *Return*
Command:

The sequence for 3D face number 5 was:

Command: 3dface   *key Return*
First point: i (Invisible)   *key Return*
                200,200,50   *key Return*
Second point: i (Invisible)   *key Return*
                300,200,50   *key Return*
Third point: i (Invisible)   *key Return*
                300,100,50   *key Return*
Fourth point: i (Invisible)   *key Return*
                200,100,50   *key Return*
Third point: *Return*
Command:

This makes all edges of 3D face number 5 invisible.

Note that the i (Invisible) must be keyed before the coordinates of
the first point of the edge to be made invisible are given. If osnaps
are to be used, being associated with the coordinates they come
after the i (Invisible).

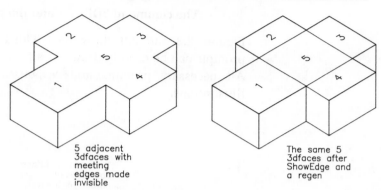

Fig. 2.7 Making **3DFACE**
edges invisible

In the **3DFACE** sub-menu (Fig. 2.2), three prompts are included below the x,y,z filters. These are **Invisibl**, **ShowEdge** and **HideEdge**. These have the following effect.

The **Invisible** prompt can be selected from this menu instead of keying *i* for invisible.

When **ShowEdge** is selected (Fig. 2.7), the following appears at the command line:

> **Command: Invisible edges will be SHOWN after next Regeneration.**
> **Command:**

If a **REGEN**eration is called thus:

> **Command:** regen *key Return*
> **Regenerating drawing.**
> **Command:**

hidden lines in 3D faces re-appear on screen.

If now **HideEdge** is selected from the **3DFACE** sub-menu:

> **Command: Invisible edges will be HIDDEN after next Regeneration.**
> **Command:**

If now a **REGEN**eration is called:

> **Command:** regen *key Return*
> **Regenerating drawing.**
> **Command:**

hidden lines disappear from the drawing.

The command 3DFACE and the prompt Third point:

Figures 2.8 and 2.9 show how **Third point:** from the **3DFACE** prompts can be used to draw extra faces adjacent to previous faces. All necessary prompts and responses are given in these two illustrations.

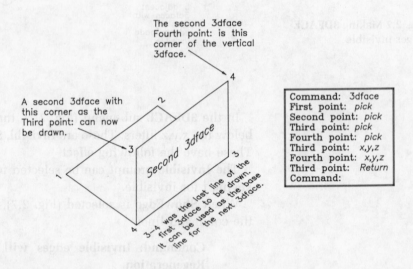

Fig. 2.8 Using **3DFACE** to construct multiple faces

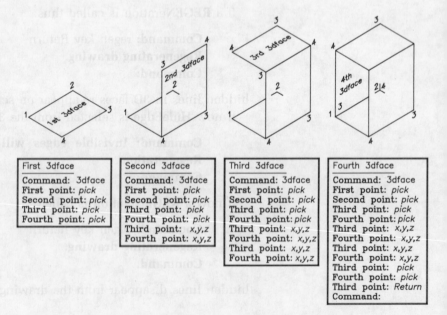

Fig. 2.9 Further multiple face construction with **3DFACE**

The SURFACE commands

The **SURFACE** commands **EDGESURF**, **REVSURF**, **RULESURF** and **TABSURF** automatically form polygon meshes, the density of the meshes being controlled by the settings of the two variables **SURFTAB1** and **SURFTAB2**. These two variables are set by:

> **Command:** surftab1   *key Return*
> **New value for SURFTAB1 <6>:** 16   *key Return*
> **Command:**
> **Command:** surftab2   *key Return*
> **New value for SURFTAB2 <6>:** 2   *key Return*
> **Command:**

In all cases both variables must be set to at least 2.

1. **EDGESURF** depends on settings of both **SURFTAB1** and **SURFTAB2**;
2. **REVSURF** depends on settings of both **SURFTAB1** and **SURFTAB2**;
3. **RULESURF** depends on setting of **SURFTAB1** with **SURFTAB2** set to at least 2;
4. **TABSURF** depends on setting of **SURFTAB1** with **SURFTAB2** set to at least 2.

Note that although **EDGSURF** and **RULSURF** show on the on-screen **SURFACES** sub-menu, the full names **EDGESURF** and **RULESURF** must be keyed when typing the commands at the keyboard.

The reader is advised to construct the examples of using **SURFACE** command which follow in order to familiarise him/herself with these methods of constructing surface meshes.

The command EDGESURF

EDGESURF will fill a closed quadrilateral with a surface mesh, the mesh sizes depending upon the settings of **SURFTAB1** and **SURFTAB2**. The quadrilateral can be coplanar or nonplanar and its sides may be lines, arcs or curves. The command will not function if any of the corners of the quadrilateral do not meet exactly. If edges do not join up the following error message will appear at the command line:

Edge 1 does not touch another edge.
Command:

and the mesh will not appear.
The sequence of prompts when **EDGESURF** is called are:

Command: edgesurf *key Return*
Select edge 1: *pick an edge of the quadrilateral*
Select edge 2: *pick an edge of the quadrilateral*
Select edge 3: *pick an edge of the quadrilateral*
Select edge 4: *pick an edge of the quadrilateral*
Command:

and the surface mesh will form automatically. As can be seen from
Fig. 2.10, the density of the mesh in both directions is dependent
upon the settings of the two **SURFTAB** variables. **SURFTAB1**
controls the density along the direction of the first edge of the
quadrilateral to be picked. **SURFTAB2** controls the density of the
mesh in the direction of the second edge to be picked.

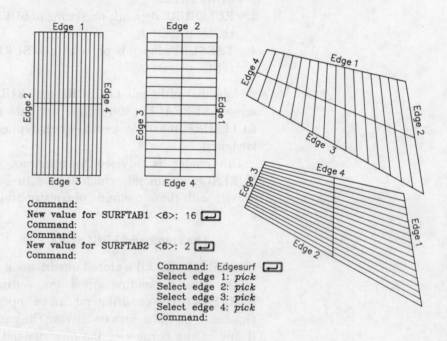

Fig. 2.10 Directions of
SURFTAB setting with
EDGESURF

```
Command:
New value for SURFTAB1 <6>: 16 [Return]
Command:
Command:
New value for SURFTAB2 <6>: 2 [Return]
Command:
```

```
Command: Edgesurf [Return]
Select edge 1: pick
Select edge 2: pick
Select edge 3: pick
Select edge 4: pick
Command:
```

Figure 2.11 shows an **EDGESURF** mesh formed within a 3D
quadrilateral formed from three lines and an arc. The drawing in
Fig. 2.11 is a **VPOINT** view of the **3D EDGESURF** surface mesh.
Figure 2.12 gives the coordinates of the four edges of the

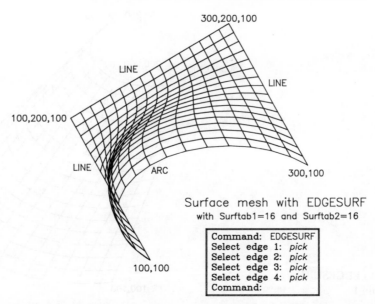

Surface mesh with EDGESURF
with Surftab1=16 and Surftab2=16

```
Command:  EDGESURF
Select edge 1:  pick
Select edge 2:  pick
Select edge 3:  pick
Select edge 4:  pick
Command:
```

Fig. 2.11 Surface mesh
constructed with
EDGESURF

quadrilateral as seen in a plan view in the WCS (World Coordinate System).

Figure 2.13 is a second example of a **3D EDGESURF** surface mesh formed within a quadrilateral of two lines and two arcs. This illustration includes the coordinates of the ends of the lines and arc and the second points of the arcs.

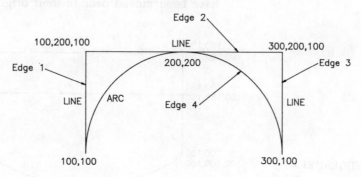

Fig. 2.12 Coordinates of the
3D outlines of Fig. 2.11

The set of four illustrations, Figs. 2.14 to 2.17, show the stages in the construction of a 3D drawing with each face involving an **EDGESURF** surface mesh.

1. Figure 2.14 is a plan view in the WCS and includes all the coordinates for constructing the quadrilaterals for the surfaces of the block.
2. Figure 2.15 is a **VPOINT** view of the quadrilaterals showing

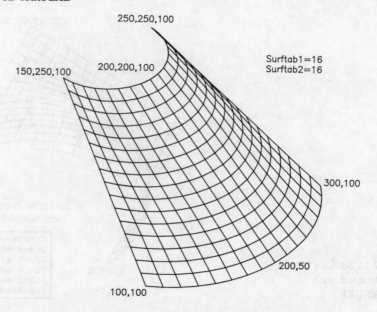

250,250,100

Surftab1=16
Surftab2=16

150,250,100   200,200,100

300,100

200,50

100,100

Fig. 2.13 **EDGESURF** –
Example 1

their re-positioning to enable edges to be easily *picked* as
prompted when the **EDGESURF** command is called.

3. Figure 2.16 shows the surface meshes added with the aid of
the **EDGESURF** command. Note the different settings of the
SURFTAB variables.

4. Figure 2.17 shows the completed block after the surface meshes
have been moved back to their original positions.

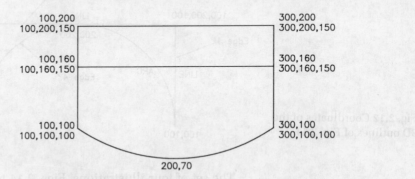

100,200
100,200,150

300,200
300,200,150

100,160
100,160,150

300,160
300,160,150

100,100
100,100,100

300,100
300,100,100

200,70

Fig. 2.14 **EDGESURF** –
Example 2; Stage 1 – 3D
outlines

The command REVSURF

The command **REVSURF** can be used to construct surface meshes
in the form of surfaces of revolution. The resulting 3D drawings
depend upon *path curves*, *axes of revolution*, and *included angles
of revolution*. The settings of the **SURFTAB** variables determines

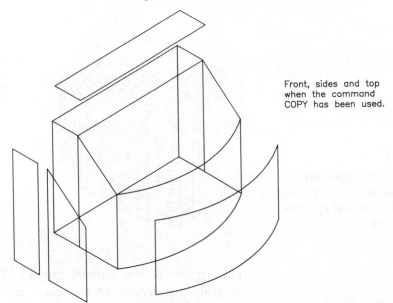

Front, sides and top
when the command
COPY has been used.

Fig. 2.15 **EDGESURF** –
Example 2, Stage 2 –
copying sides

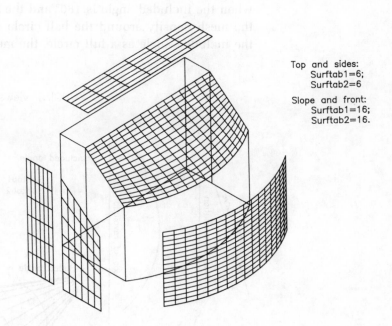

Top and sides:
  Surftab1=6;
  Surftab2=6

Slope and front:
  Surftab1=16;
  Surftab2=16.

Fig. 2.16 **EDGESURF** –
Example 2; Stage 3 –
applying surface meshes

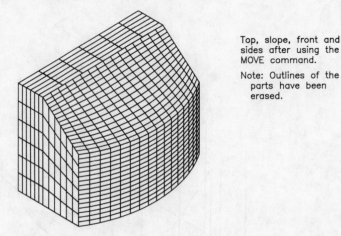

Top, slope, front and sides after using the MOVE command.

Note: Outlines of the parts have been erased.

Fig. 2.17 **EDGESURF** – Example 2; Stage 4 – moving surface meshes into final position

the density of the surface meshes. The setting of **SURFTAB1** controls the density of the mesh around its circular path. The setting of **SURFTAB2** determines the density of the mesh in the direction of the axis of revolution. Note that the mesh density around the circular path is the same as the **SURFTAB1** setting irrespective of the included angle. Thus, as can be seen in Fig. 2.18, when the included angle is 180° and the **SURFTAB1** setting is 24, the mesh density around the half circle of revolution is 24. With the included angle as a full circle, the mesh density is still 24.

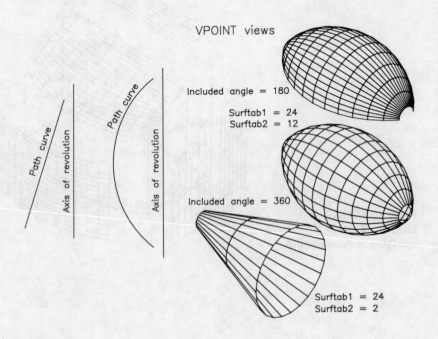

VPOINT views

Path curve

Axis of revolution

Path curve

Axis of revolution

Included angle = 180

Surftab1 = 24
Surftab2 = 12

Included angle = 360

Surftab1 = 24
Surftab2 = 2

Fig. 2.18 **REVSURF** and associated **SURFACE** settings

When **REVSURF** is called the prompts at the command line follow the pattern:

>**Command:** revsurf   *key Return*
>**Select path curve:**   *pick*
>**Select axis of revolution:**   *pick*
>**Start angle <0>:**   *Return*
>**Included angle (+=ccw, −=cw) <Full circle>:**   *Return*
>**Command:**

and the surface of revolution forms.

Figure 2.19 is an example of a **REVSURF** surface mesh, showing its construction. Figure 2.20 is a **VPOINT** view of the surface mesh after **HIDE** has been called. Note the erasure of the axis of revolution once the surface mesh appears on screen.

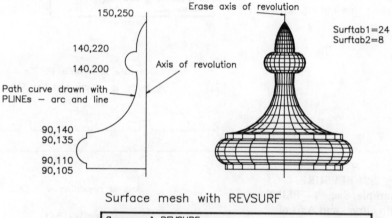

Surface mesh with REVSURF

```
Command: REVSURF
Select path curve: pick
Select axis of revolution: pick
Start angle <0>: Return
Included angle (+=ccw, −=cw) <Full circle>: Return
Command:
```

Fig. 2.19 Coordinates for a surface mesh constructed with **REVSURF**

Figures 2.21 and 2.22 show the construction details and a **VPOINT** view of an axle and pulley drawn as surface meshes with the aid of **REVSURF**. Note that the path curves in this example are continuous plines. This is necessary to enable a single path curve to be *picked* in response to the prompts. If the path curve had been constructed from lines and arcs, each separate line and arc would have to be *picked* to form the surface mesh.

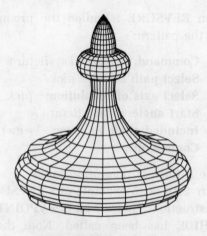

Fig. 2.20 **VPOINT** of the
surface mesh of Fig. 2.19

```
Command:  VPOINT
Rotate\<View point>:  0,0.3,-1
Regenerating  drawing:
Command:
```

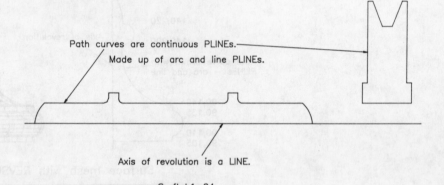

Path curves are continuous PLINEs.
Made up of arc and line PLINEs.

Fig. 2.21 **REVSURF** –
Example; Stage 1 – **PLINE**
path curves and Axis of
revolution

Axis of revolution is a LINE.

Surftab1=24
Surftab2=2

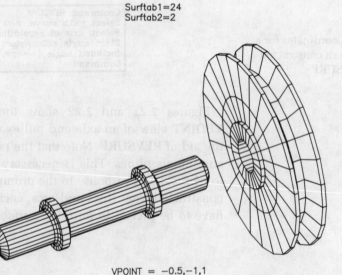

Fig. 2.22 **REVSURF** –
Example; Stage 2 – **VPOINT**
of surface of revolution

VPOINT = -0.5,-1,1

The command RULESURF

RULESURF will form surface meshes between two lines or curves. The density of the mesh is determined solely by the setting of **SURFTAB1**, although **SURFTAB2** must be set to at least 2 for the command to function. Figure 2.23 shows both the coordinates of two 3D arcs, the commands and prompts and the resulting surface mesh when the arcs have been selected. Figure 2.24 is a **VPOINT** view of the resulting surface mesh after **HIDE** has been called. The prompts associated with this command are:

> **Command:** rulesurf   *key Return*
> **Select first defining curve:**   *pick*
> **Select second defining curve:**   *pick*
> **Command:**

and the surface mesh forms.

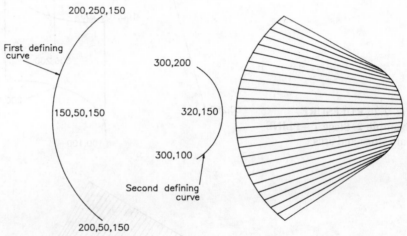

Command: RULESURF
Select first defining curve: *pick*
Select second defining curve: *pick*
Command:

Fig. 2.23 **RULESURF** –
Example 1 – defining curves
and surface mesh

Surface mesh with RULESURF
with Surftab1=24 and Surftab2=2

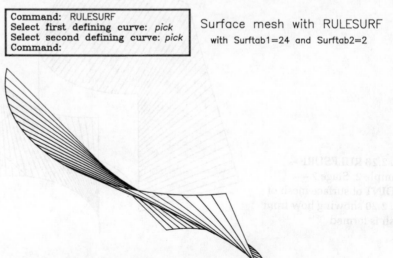

Fig. 2.24 **RULESURF** –
VPOINT view of Fig. 2.23

Figures 2.25 to 2.27 show stages in producing a block made up from **RULESURF** surface meshes:

1. Figure 2.25: draw the necessary defining curves.
2. Figure 2.26: copy the two front arcs to make their selection as defining curves easier. Complete all **RULESURF** surfaces.
3. Figure 2.27: move the front surface mesh back into its position. Use osnaps to ensure exact positioning of the mesh.

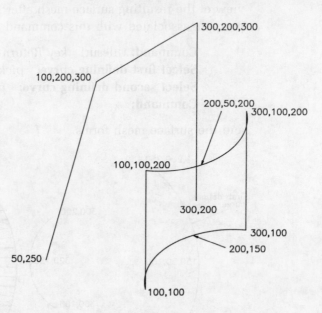

Fig. 2.25 **RULESURF** –
Example 2; Stage 1 – **PLINE**
path lines and arcs

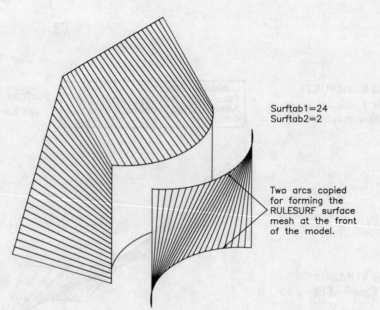

Surftab1=24
Surftab2=2

Two arcs copied
for forming the
RULESURF surface
mesh at the front
of the model.

Fig. 2.26 **RULESURF** –
Example 2; Stage 2 –
VPOINT of surface mesh of
Fig. 2.20 showing how front
mesh is formed

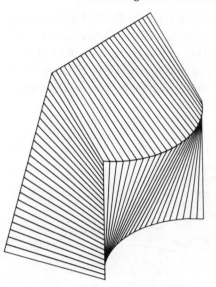

Fig. 2.27 **RULESURF** –
Example 2; Stage 3 –
VPOINT of surface mesh of
Fig. 2.20 with front mesh
moved to its required
position

The command TABSURF

2D PLINE outlines can be extruded with the aid of **TABSURF** to
form surface meshes. The extrusions so produced can be compared
with those formed with the aid of the command **ELEV**ation.
However, whereas **ELEV**ation extrusions can only occur perpen-
dicularly to the plane on which the 2D outline is drawn, **TABSURF**
extrusions can be taken at any angle to the plane. Figure 2.28 shows
a pline arcs and lines outline, together with a direction vector
drawn at an angle, not perpendicular to the x,y plane. Figure 2.29
shows the resulting **TABSURF** extrusion of the outline along the
route indicated by the direction vector. The sequence of prompts in
response to the command are:

> **Command:** tabsurf   *key Return*
> **Select path curve:**   *pick*
> **Select direction vector:**   *pick*
> **Command:**

and the extrusion is formed on screen.

Notes:

1. The direction vector need not be inside or at all close to the
   pline outline to be extruded.
2. The length of the extrusion is governed by the length of the
   direction vector.
3. Only the **SURFTAB1** setting affects the density of the resulting

surface mesh. **SURFTAB2** must be set to a figure of 2 or greater, although the variable has no effect on the resulting extrusion.

4. The top surface of a **TABSURF** extrusion does not contain a surface mesh. Thus **HIDE** has no effect on hiding lines behind the upper face of the extrusion.

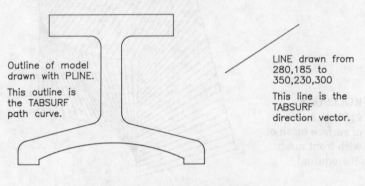

Outline of model
drawn with PLINE.

This outline is
the TABSURF
path curve.

LINE drawn from
280,185 to
350,230,300

This line is the
TABSURF
direction vector.

Surface mesh with TABSURF
With Surftab1=4 and Surftab2=2

```
Command:  TABSURF
Select path curve: pick
Select direction vector: pick
Command:
```

Fig. 2.28 **TABSURF** –
Example 1; Stage 1 – **PLINE**
outline and direction vector

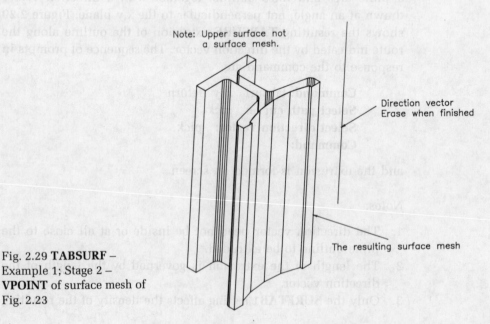

Note: Upper surface not
a surface mesh.

Direction vector
Erase when finished

The resulting surface mesh

Fig. 2.29 **TABSURF** –
Example 1; Stage 2 –
VPOINT of surface mesh of
Fig. 2.23

Figures 2.30 and 2.31 show further examples of **TABSURF** extrusions from a variety of pline outlines and direction vectors.

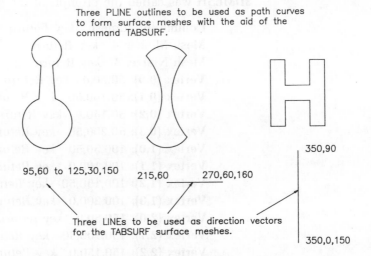

Three PLINE outlines to be used as path curves to form surface meshes with the aid of the command TABSURF.

95,60 to 125,30,150   215,60   270,60,160

350,90

350,0,150

Three LINEs to be used as direction vectors for the TABSURF surface meshes.

Fig. 2.30 **TABSURF –** Example 2; Stage 1 – **PLINE** outlines of three shapes

In each example Surftab1=16 and Surftab2=2

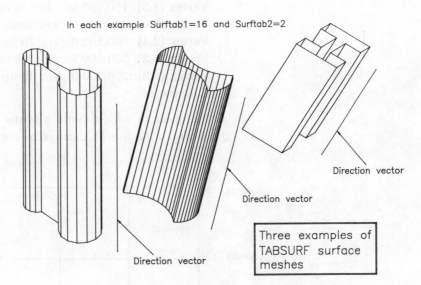

Direction vector

Direction vector

Direction vector

Three examples of TABSURF surface meshes

Fig. 2.31 **TABSURF –** Example 2; Stage 2 – the three surface meshes of Fig. 2.30

The commands 3DMESH and 3DPOLY

Surface meshes can be constructed most easily with the **SURFACE** commands mentioned previously. The two command systems **3DMESH** and **3DPOLY** are included in the AutoCAD system for those operators who wish to produce AutoLISP applications or other forms of macro. Thus only a very limited description of methods of constructing with these two commands is included here

The command 3DMESH

To produce the 3D mesh shown in Figs 2.32 and 2.33, when **3DMESH** was called the prompts at the command line were:

Command: 3dmesh *key Return*
Mesh M size: 4 *key Return*
Mesh N size: 4 *key Return*
Vertex (0,0): 50,50,0 *key Return*
Vertex (0,1): 50,100,50 *key Return*
Vertex (0,2): 50,150,0 *key Return*
Vertex (0,3): 50,200,50 *key Return*
Vertex (1,0): 100,50,50 *key Return*
Vertex (1,1): 100,100,0 *key Return*
Vertex (1,2): 100,150,50 *key Return*
Vertex (1,3): 100,200,0 *key Return*
Vertex (2,0): 150,50,0 *key Return*
Vertex (2,1): 150,100,50 *key Return*
Vertex (2,2): 150,150,0 *key Return*
Vertex (2,3): 150,200,50 *key Return*
Vertex (3,0): 200,50,50 *key Return*
Vertex (3,1): 200,100,0 *key Return*
Vertex (3,2): 200,150,50 *key Return*
Vertex (3,3): 200,200,0 *key Return*
Command:

Note the order in which vertices of the M and N mesh sizes are keyed. In Fig. 2.32 the M mesh size corresponds to the vertical

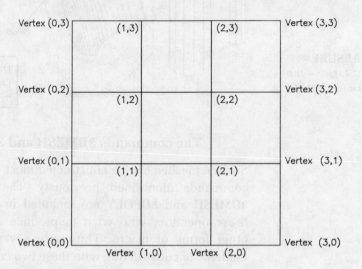

Fig. 2.32 Plan view in the WCS of a 4 × 4 surface mesh formed with **3DMESH**

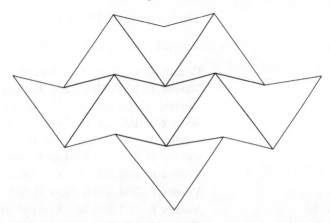

Fig. 2.33 **VPOINT** view of
the surface mesh of Fig. 2.32

vertices and N mesh size corresponds to the horizontal vertices.
Figure 2.33 is a **VPOINT** view of the resulting mesh. Note that the
mesh numbers refer to the number of lines each way in the surface
mesh.

The command 3DPOLY

The command **PLINE** can only be used in one plane. It cannot
therefore be called to draw a 3D polyline. 3D polylines can be
drawn with the aid of the **3DPOLY** command. When the command
is called, the command line shows:

> **Command:** 3dpoly   *key Return*
> **From point:** *pick or give 3D coordinates   key Return*
> **Close/Undo/<Endpoint of line>:** *pick or give 3D coor-*
>   *dinates   key Return*
> **Close/Undo/<Endpoint of line>:** *pick or give 3D coor-*
>   *dinates   key Return*
> **Close/Undo/<Endpoint of line>:** *pick or give 3D coor-*
>   *dinates   key Return*
> **Close/Undo/<Endpoint of line>:** *pick or give 3D coor-*
>   *dinates   key Return*

and continue picking and keying points or coordinates until either
the line is completed without closing (press *Return*) or, as a closed
pline by keying *c* (*Close*). Keying *u* (*Undo*) will undo the last part of
the pline to be drawn. Note that the width of a **3DPOLY** line cannot
be changed. It is always of zero thickness. Neither are arcs possible
with this command.

The command PFACE (Figs 2.34 and 2.35)

This command follows the pattern:

Command: pface   *key Return*
Vertex 1: 100,300,0   *key Return*
Vertex 2: 100,200,50   *key Return*
Vertex 3: 100,100,0   *key Return*
Vertex 4: 200,100,50   *key Return*
Vertex 5: 300,100,0   *key Return*
Vertex 6: 300,200,50   *key Return*
Vertex 7: 300,300,0   *key Return*
Vertex 8: 200,300,50   *key Return*
Vertex 9:   *Return*
Face 1, vertex 1: 1   *key Return*
Face 1, vertex 2: 2   *key Return*
Face 1, vertex 3: 3   *key Return*
Face 1, vertex 4: 4   *key Return*
Face 1, vertex 5: 5   *key Return*
Face 1, vertex 6: 6   *key Return*
Face 1, vertex 7: 7   *key Return*
Face 1, vertex 8: 8   *key Return*
Face 1, vertex 9: 1   *key Return*
Face 1, vertex 10:   *Return*
Face 2, vertex 1: 1   *key Return*
Face 2, vertex 2: 8   *key Return*
Face 2, vertex 3: 7   *key Return*
Face 2, vertex 4: 2   *key Return*
Face 2, vertex 5: 1   *key Return*
Face 2, vertex 6:   *Return*
Face 3, vertex 1: 2   *key Return*
Face 3, vertex 2: 3   *key Return*
Face 3, vertex 3: 4   *key Return*
Face 3, vertex 4: 5   *key Return*
Face 3, vertex 5: 6   *key Return*
Face 3, vertex 6: 1   *key Return*
Face 3, vertex 7:   *Return*
Face 4, vertex 1:   *Return*
Command:

and the whole set of three polyfaces appears on screen – Figs 2.34 and 2.35.

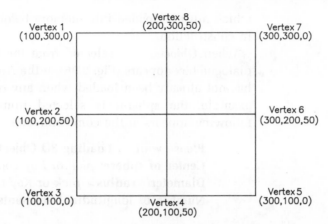

Vertex 1
(100,300,0)

Vertex 8
(200,300,50)

Vertex 7
(300,300,0)

Vertex 2
(100,200,50)

Vertex 6
(300,200,50)

Fig. 2.34 Plan view in the
WCS of a surface mesh
formed with **PFACE**

Vertex 3
(100,100,0)

Vertex 4
(200,100,50)

Vertex 5
(300,100,0)

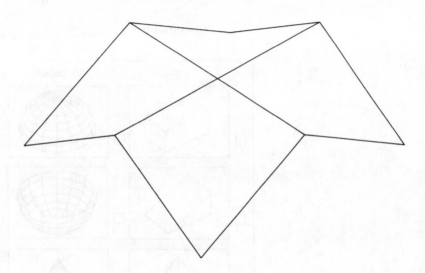

Fig. 2.35 **VPOINT** view of
the mesh of Fig. 2.34

3D OBJECTS

The **SURFACES on**-screen menu given in Fig. 2.2 includes the
command **3D OBJECTS**. The command can also be called from the
pull-down menu, where it appears as **Objects. . .** (Fig. 2.3). When
the command is selected from the on-screen menu, the command
lines shows:

Please wait. . . Loading 3D Objects.
Command:

A short time elapses and the **3D OBJECTS** are loaded into
memory. They are held in an AutoLISP file *3d.lsp*, the contents of

which must be loaded into memory before the objects can be used in constructions.

When **Objects...** is selected from the **Draw** pull-down menu a dialogue box appears (Fig. 2.36). If the AutoLISP file for the objects has not already been loaded when any one of the objects (in this example, the sphere) is selected from the dialogue box, the following appears at the command line:

> **Please wait... Loading 3D Objects.**
> **Center of sphere:** *pick* or *Key* coordinates
> **Diameter/<radius>** *pick* or *Key* coordinates
> **Number of longitudinal segments <16>:** *Return* or *Key* a figure
> **Number of latitudinal segments <16>:** *Return* or *Key* a figure
>
> **Command:**

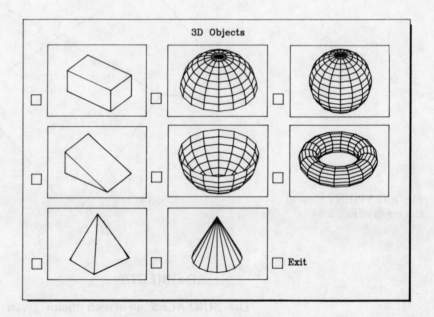

Fig. 2.36 The **3D Objects** dialogue box

and the 3D sphere appears on screen. Similar prompts appear for the other 3D objects. Figure 2.37 shows all the 3D objects which can be constructed. When constructing 3D model drawings involving **3D OBJECTS**, the command prompts for each object are easy to follow.

Some 3D model drawings can be constructed either wholly or partly from **3D OBJECTS**. Two examples are given in Fig. 2.38

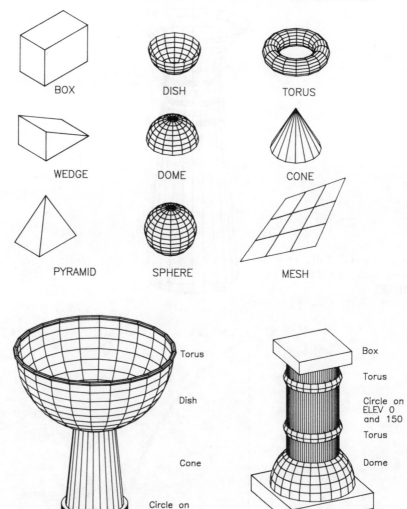

Fig. 2.37 **VPOINT** drawings of each of the 3D objects

Fig. 2.38 Two 3D model drawings formed from 3D objects and cylinders from circles in **ELEV**

Figure 2.39 is a **REVSURF** drawing of a vase. The **PLINE** from which the 3D drawing was revolved is given in Fig. 2.40. The procedure for drawing the **PLINE** was:

1. The **PLINE** was drawn to the required outline;
2. The **PLINE** was offset at 0.5 units;
3. The upper ends of the **PLINE** were joined by a pline arc;
4. The three plines – the two plines plus the pline arc – were joined with the aid of the **PEDIT** command;
5. The solid of revolution was then formed with **REVSURF**.

Fig. 2.39 **VPOINT** of a vase
drawn with the aid of
SOLREV

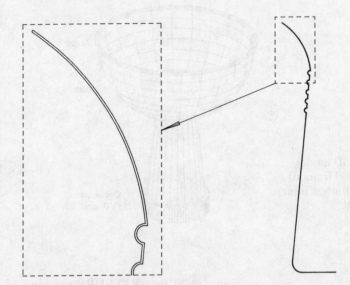

Fig. 2.40 The **PLINE**s on
which Fig. 2.39 are based

Figure 2.41 is an example of a 3D drawing constructed from
RULESURF surface meshes.

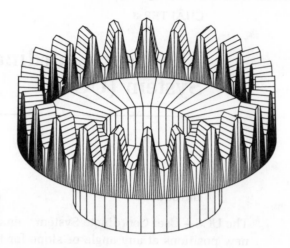

Fig. 2.41 An example of a 3D
solid drawing constructed
with **EDGESURF**

CHAPTER 3

The User Coordinate
System (UCS)

Introduction

The UCS – User Coordinate System – enables the user to determine new positions at any angle or slope for the x,y plane on which to construct drawings. This allows details to be constructed on a new UCS surface as if working in the original x,y plane (World Coordinate System or WCS). To work freely within the UCS, the two system variables **UCSICON** and **UCSFOLLOW** must be set.

The variable UCSICON

Command: setvar   *key Return*
Variable name or ?: UCSICON   *key Return*
New value for UCSICON <0>: 3   *key Return*
Command:

If set at 1, the icon is displayed at the WCS origin or as near as is possible to the WCS origin.

If set to 3, the icon is displayed at the UCS origin, no matter where the origin is set.

The UCSicon can be turned on or off as follows:

Command: ucsicon   *Keyboard Return*
ON/OFF/All/Noorigin/ORigin <OFF>: on   *Keyboard*
Return

Command:

The prompts have the following meanings:

1. **ON** – the UCS icon appears on screen;
2. **OFF** – the UCS icon disappears from the screen;
3. **All** – when working in viewports (see page 66), the UCS icon will appear in, or disappear from, all viewports, if **all** is given as a response *after* the icon is turned **ON** or **OFF**;
4. Noorigin – when **n** is *keyed* as a response, the icon goes to as

near to the bottom left corner of the screen as is possible;

5. **OR**igin – key **or** and the icon goes to the actual origin (0,0,0), no matter where it is on screen. Note that the origin can be changed by stating an x,y coordinate as a response to this option for a new origin, when the icon will appear at this new origin.

The UCS icon

The UCS icon takes a variety of forms, as is shown in Fig. 3.1, according to the setting of the UCS. If the UCS is set so that it can only be viewed from edge on, or nearly edge on, a broken pencil icon appears on screen. This gives a warning to the operator that the UCS may have been set wrongly, or that the system variable **UCSFOLLOW** is not **ON** (1). Note the PSpace icon in Fig. 3.1, details of which will be given in Chapter 4.

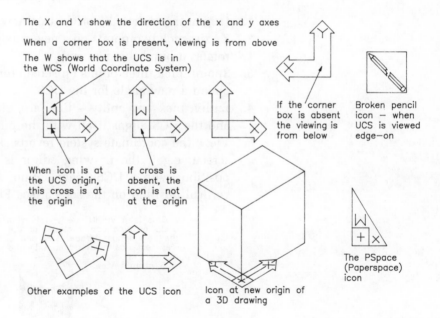

The X and Y show the direction of the x and y axes

When a corner box is present, viewing is from above

The W shows that the UCS is in the WCS (World Coordinate System)

If the corner box is absent the viewing is from below

Broken pencil icon – when UCS is viewed edge–on

When icon is at the UCS origin, this cross is at the origin

If cross is absent, the icon is not at the origin

The PSpace (Paperspace) icon

Fig. 3.1 The UCS icons in a variety of forms

Other examples of the UCS icon

Icon at new origin of a 3D drawing

The variable UCSFOLLOW

The variable is set by one or the other of the two methods:

Command: setvar   *Keyboard Return*
Variable name or ?: ucsfollow   *key Return*
New value for UCSFOLLOW <0>: 1   *key Return*
Command:

or:

> **Command:** ucsfollow   *key Return*
> **New value for UCSFOLLOW <0>:** 1   *key Return*
> **Command:**

If set at 0, the UCS remains in the World Coordinate System (WCS) position – it fails to respond to answers to the UCS command prompts. If set at 1, the UCS will be reset in response to answers to the UCS command prompts.

The command UCS

> **Command:** ucs   *Keyboard Return*
> **Origin/ZAxis/3point/Entity/View/X/Y/Z/Prev/Restore/Save**
> **/Del/?/<World>:**

The UCS prompts have the following meanings:

1. **Origin:** this resets the origin to a new *keyed* or *picked* point.
2. **ZAxis:** *pick* two points on a new z axis and the UCS x,y plane rotates around this new axis.
3. **3point:** *pick* three points on screen (or *key* the coordinates) to obtain a new angle for the UCS.
4. **Entity:** *pick* any entity – line, arc, circle, edge of plane etc., and the UCS aligns itself with the *picked* entity.
5. **View:** the coordinate system reverts as if perpendicular to the screen, e.g if the drawing editor is in a VPOINT viewing position, with a UCS View option, text can be added in a vertical position on the screen (see Fig. 3.2.)

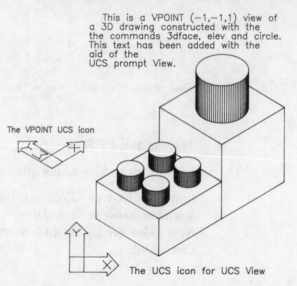

Fig. 3.2 A **VPOINT** view in the UCS view

6. **X/Y/Z:** keying either of these, followed by keying an angle, places the UCS at an angle to the x, y or z axes.
7. **Prev:** this brings up the last UCS to be used.
8. **Restore:** this restores a named UCS.
9. **Save:** this saves a UCS by name in the drawing.
10. **Del:** this deletes a named UCS.
11. **?:** and pressing *Return* twice, brings a list such as that shown below, of previously saved UCS planes on screen.

> **Current UCS: *WORLD***
> **Saved coordinate systems:**
> **DOOR**
> > Origin = <150,100,0>, X Axis = <1,1,0>
> > Y Axis = <0,0,1>, Z Axis = <1,−1,0>
> **FRONT**
> > Origin = <130,100,0>, X Axis = <1,0,0>
> > Y Axis = <0,0,1>, Z Axis = <0,−1,0>
> **LEFT**
> > Origin = <130,100,0>, X Axis = <0,1,0>
> > Y Axis = <0,0,1>, Z Axis = <1,0,0>
> **RIGHT**
> > Origin = <240,100,0>, X Axis = <0,1,0>
> > Y Axis = <0,0,1>, Z Axis = <1,0,0>
> **ROOF**
> > Origin = <240,100,0>, X Axis = <0,1,1>
> > Y Axis = <1,0,0>, Z Axis = <0,1,−1>
> — **Press RETURN for more** —
> **ROOF1**
> > Origin = <240,155,125>, X Axis = <0,1,−1>
> > Y Axis = <1,0,0>, Z Axis = <0,−1,−1>

12. **World:** this restores the World Coordinate System.

Note: after setting any new UCS, *Zoom* to 1 to ensure the new UCS fits into the drawing editor screen.

Warning

If care is not taken when setting a new UCS, the results may not be as expected. An example of problems which may arise is given in Figs 3.3 and 3.4. As can be seen from Fig. 3.3, if, while in the WCS (World Coordinate System), a UCS 3point is required, the new UCS comes up as expected when a positive value for the z coordinate is entered. That is − in the new UCS (really a front view of the 3D boxes) – the boxes appear *above* the WCS x,y plane. Note that the responses to the UCS option 3point in this case will be:

Command: ucs   *key Return*
Origin/ZAxis/3point/Entity/View/X/Y/Z/Prev/Restore/
            Save/Del/?/<World>: 3 (3point)   *key Return*
Origin point <0,0,0>:   *Return*
Point on positive portion of the X-Axis <1,0,0>:   *Return*
Point on positive-Y portion of the UCS X-Y plane <0,1,0>:
                        0,0,1   *key Return*
Regenerating drawing
Command: z (zoom)
All/Center/Dynamic/Extents/Left/Previous/Vmax/Window/
                    <Scale(X/XP)>: 1   *key Return*
Command:

If a negative value for the z coordinate is entered, the boxes appear below the WCS x,y plane.

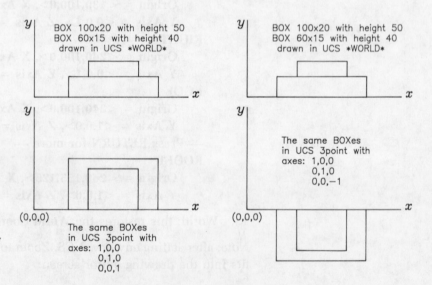

Fig. 3.3 Problems which may arise when setting a new UCS with 3point

If a new ucs 3point is required when a new UCS has appeared on screen, with the same boxes as were drawn in the WCS, the boxes will appear above the x,y plane in the WCS only if a negative value for the z coordinate is entered. This is shown in Fig. 3.4.

The same precautions apply when rotating about x, y, z, in response to the **X/Y/Z/** options of the UCS command system. A positive angle will probably be necessary in most cases.

This is because positive rotation of the x,y plane around the x, y

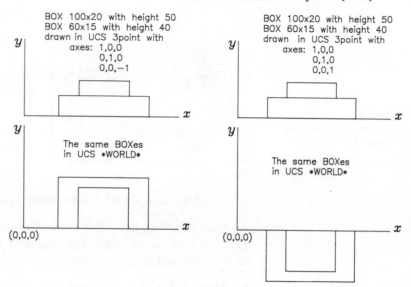

Fig. 3.4 Further problems
with the 3point option

or z axes will be in an anti-clockwise direction looking towards the
origin (0,0,0). The direction of rotation is covered by the right-hand
rule:

The right-hand rule

Imagine you are gripping the axis in your right hand and the thumb
of that hand is pointing towards the direction of the positive value
of the axis (away from the origin). Your fingers will be wrapped
around the axis. The tips of your fingers are pointing in the positive
direction of rotation.

Calling new a new User Coordinate System

As can be seen above, a new UCS can be called and set by *keying*
responses to the **UCS** command at the command line. Another –
possibly quicker – method is to *pick* **UCS Control. . .** from the
Settings pull-down menu. This results in the **UCS Control** dialogue
box appearing on screen, from which one can *pick* a current UCS
from those already set. If a new UCS is required, *picking* **Define
new current UCS** from the **UCS Control** dialogue box brings the
Define New User Coordinate System dialogue box on screen. A
new current UCS can be defined in this box. This new UCS will be
added to the list in the **UCS Control** dialogue box. Figure 3.5 shows
both these dialogue boxes.

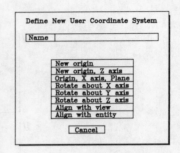

Fig. 3.5 The UCS **Control** and **New UCS** dialogue boxes

An example of 3D drawing with the aid of the UCS

An example of some of the various settings of the UCS is given in Figs 3.6 and 3.7 showing the stages of drawing a 3D model of a simple electronics control box.

1. Stage 1: Fig. 3.6, Drawing 1. A VPOINT view of the outline of the box, including overall dimensions, has been drawn in the WCS (UCS – World) with 3D faces.
2. Stage 2: Fig. 3.6, Drawing 2. By setting **ELEV** at various settings, draw the three parts of the aerial.
3. Stage 3: Fig. 3.6, Drawing 3. Procedure:
    (a) Call **UCS**, *Key X*, set at 30;
    (b) Call **UCS**, *Key Y*, set at 30;
    (c) Call **UCS**, *Key 3*, pick points 1, 2, and 3 in response to the prompts which follow. This results in the UCS being set

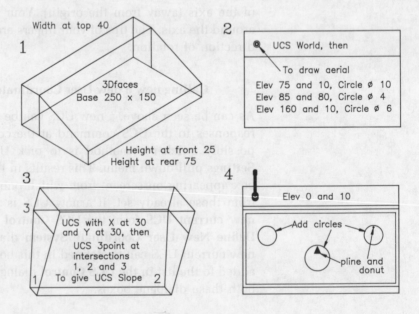

Fig. 3.6 Stages 1 to 4 in constructing a 3D model with the aid of the UCS

with the sloping face flat on the screen surface. Use osnaps if necessary (Drawing 4 of Fig. 3.4).

4. Stage 4: Fig. 3.6, Drawing 4. Follow the stages:
   (a) In this UCS set **ELEV** to 0 and 10 and add the control circles;
   (b) set **ELEV** to 10 and 0 and add doughnut and pline triangle to the tops of the control knobs.
5. Stage 5: Fig 3.7, Drawing 5. Set **ELEV** to 0 and 0 and add details of control settings and the pline box and text.
6. Stage 6: Fig. 3.5, Drawing 6. Call **UCS World**. Set **ELEV** to 75 and 0. Add pline box and text.
7. Stage 7. Fig. 3.7, Drawing 7. Set **ELEV** back to 0 and 0. Call VPOINT and Key −1,−1,1. Call **HIDE**.

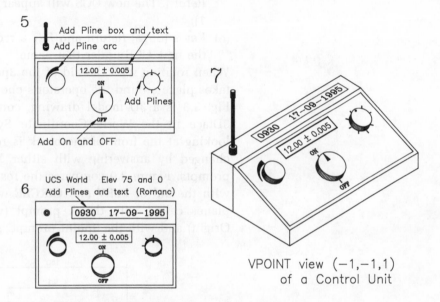

Fig. 3.7 Stages 5 and 6 in constructing a 3D model in the UCS

VPOINT view (−1,−1,1) of a Control Unit

Notes on the UCS

1. The system variable **UCSFOLLOW** must be **ON** (1) in order that a new UCS can be set.
2. If the ucsicon is to indicate the Origin of a new UCS, the system variable **UCSICON** must be set **ON** and to 3.
3. When a new UCS has been selected − by using any of the prompts − call **ZOOM** and key 1, in order to re-scale the resulting drawing on screen.
4. No matter which prompt has been employed, the Origin (0,0,0) will rarely be in the same screen position as when in the WCS.

If determining points by means of coordinates in a new UCS, check where the Origin is.

5. When rotating the UCS through 90° with the aid of the **X**, **Y** or **Z** prompts, the UCS will be rotated through 90° around the *x*, *y* or *z* screen axes, unless a new Origin is selected after answering *o* (Origin) to the UCS prompts. The result of not selecting a new Origin for an x-axis rotation is shown in Fig. 3.9.

6. When rotating the UCS around the x-axis, the UCS prompts need to be answered twice (or even three times):

   (a) set a new origin by *Keying o* (Origin) *Return* and *picking* the required new origin. This sets the origin and the icon appears at the new selected origin (if **UCSICON** is set at 3);

   (b) *Key X Return*, then *Key* the required angle of rotation *Return*. The new UCS will appear (if **UCSFOLLOW** is set at 1);

   (c) *Key s* (Save) *Return* and *Key* a required UCS name to save the new UCS under that name.

7. When rotating with the aid of the **3point** prompt, the rotation takes place around the operator's chosen axis. As an example, Fig. 3.8 is a 3D model drawing, constructed with the aid of 3Dface in the World Coordinate System (WCS). If a view looking at the front of the block is required, the UCS can be changed by answering with either X or 3point to the UCS prompts. Figure 3.9 compares the results of adding a cylinder with the aid of **ELEV** and **CIRCLE** while in each of the UCS planes called with the **X** prompt (without selecting a new Origin) and with the **3point** prompt.

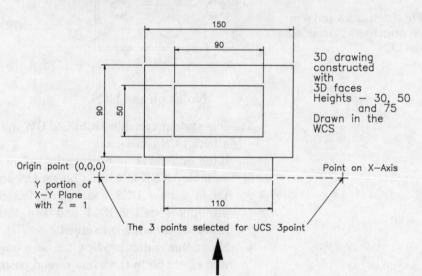

Fig. 3.8 Selection of points
for a 3point UCS

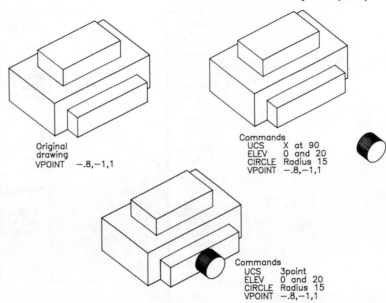

Original
drawing
VPOINT   −.8,−1,1

Commands
UCS   X at 90
ELEV   0 and 20
CIRCLE   Radius 15
VPOINT   −.8,−1,1

Commands
UCS   3point
ELEV   0 and 20
CIRCLE   Radius 15
VPOINT   −.8,−1,1

Fig. 3.9 Possible errors in using the X option of the UCS

8. When using the **3point** prompt:
    (a) A rubber band connected to each of the first two points selected keeps the operator aware of the previous selections.
    (b) If selecting the three points while in the WCS, the first two points can be *picked*, then select the filter **.xy**, then, when **(need Z)** appears, *keying* any number will set the new 3point UCS. As with **VPOINT**, the coordinate number keyed indicates only the direction of the required axis, not its length. The final prompt in the 3point series is:

    Point on the positive-Y portion of the X-axis:

    which can be answered with any figure – e.g. the figure 1.

    Figure 3.10 shows the on-screen sub-menus for the UCS options.

Exercises

This group of exercises is included here to allow the reader to practise the 3D commands explained in this chapter and in Chapter 2, by constructing a number of simple 3D drawings. Short instructions are included with either the text below or with the illustrations accompanying the exercises.

1. Figure 3.11 is a drawing of a tenon on the end of a block. Construct the 3D drawing Fig. 3.9 with the aid of the **3DFACE**

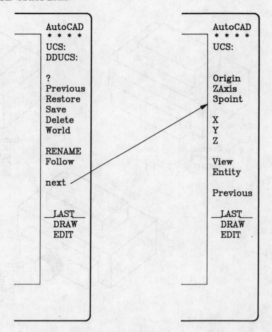

Fig. 3.10 The UCS on-screen
sub-menus

command. Then place the drawing in a pictorial view with
VPOINT and **HIDE** lines behind the 3Dfaces.

2.   Construct the 3D drawing Fig. 3.12. Follow the details of sizes
     and commands included with the given drawing.

3.   Construct the 3D drawing Fig. 3.13. Follow the details of sizes
     and commands included with the given drawing.

4.   Construct the given drawing, Fig. 3.14, with the aid of the
     command **3DFACE**. Use the **Invisible** option of the **3DFACE**

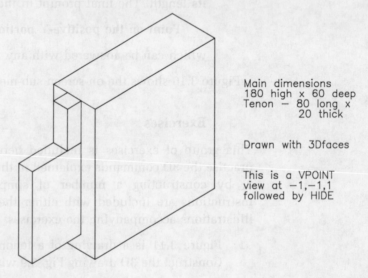

Main dimensions
180 high x 60 deep
Tenon — 80 long x
          20 thick

Drawn with 3Dfaces

This is a VPOINT
view at −1,−1,1
followed by HIDE

Fig. 3.11 Exercise 1

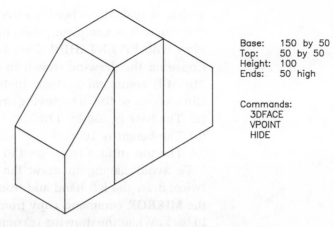

Base: 150 by 50
Top: 50 by 50
Height: 100
Ends: 50 high

Commands:
  3DFACE
  VPOINT
  HIDE

Fig. 3.12 Exercise 2

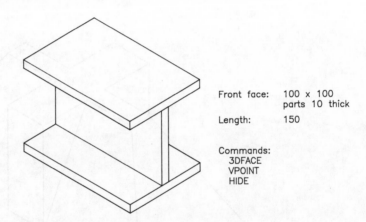

Front face: 100 x 100
              parts 10 thick
Length: 150

Commands:
  3DFACE
  VPOINT
  HIDE

Fig. 3.13 Exercise 3

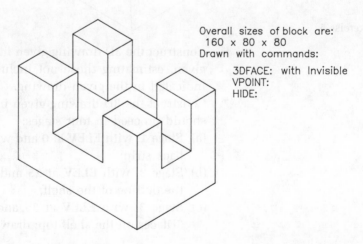

Overall sizes of block are:
160 x 80 x 80
Drawn with commands:

  3DFACE: with Invisible
  VPOINT:
  HIDE:

Fig. 3.14 Exercise 4

system to make lines between the 3Dfaces invisible. When the construction is complete, place the 3D drawing in a pictorial view with **VPOINT**. **HIDE** lines behind the 3D faces.

5. Construct the drawing shown in Fig.3.15 with the aid of the **3DFACE** command system, including the **Invisible** option. Dimensions of the 3D drawing are:

   (a) The base is 260 by 120;

   (b) The height is 100;

   (c) The top surface faces are 120 by 40 and 140 by 20.

   To avoid having to draw the sloping and vertical faces twice, draw the left-hand and front faces, then with the aid of the **MIRROR** command copy from left to right and from front to back. When the drawing is completed, place it in a pictorial view with **VPOINT** and **HIDE** lines behind the 3Dfaces.

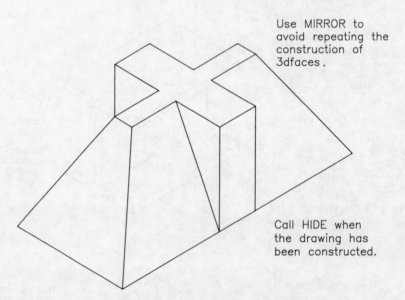

Use MIRROR to avoid repeating the construction of 3dfaces.

Call HIDE when the drawing has been constructed.

Fig. 3.15 Exercise 5

6. Construct the 3D drawing given in Fig. 3.16. Work to the sizes given, estimating those not included. Use the commands as indicated in the given drawing.

7. Construct the 3D drawing given in Fig. 3.17; the construction should proceed in four stages:

   (a) Stage 1: with **ELEV** at 0 and with thickness 25 to draw the back strip;

   (b) Stage 2: with **ELEV** at 25 and with thickness 10 to draw the outline of the shelf;

   (c) Stage 3: with **ELEV** at 35 and with thickness 0 to draw 3Dfaces on the shelf top; draw the left-hand half, with the

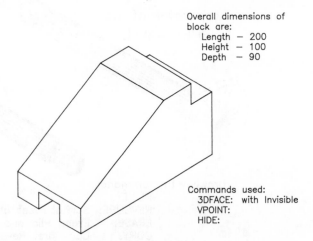

Overall dimensions of
block are:
    Length — 200
    Height — 100
    Depth — 90

Commands used:
    3DFACE: with Invisible
    VPOINT:
    HIDE:

Fig. 3.16 Exercise 6

Invisible option where necessary, then **MIRROR** the right-hand half from the left hand;

(d) Stage 4: view the drawing with **VPOINT** at −1,−1,1 and **HIDE** lines behind the 3Dfaces and the extrusions.

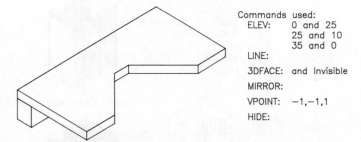

Commands used:
    ELEV: 0 and 25
             25 and 10
             35 and 0
    LINE:
    3DFACE: and Invisible
    MIRROR:
    VPOINT: −1,−1,1
    HIDE:

Fig. 3.17 Exercise 7

8. Two views of a poppet valve are given in Fig. 3.18. Construct the poppet valve drawing, following the details given with the drawing.

9. Views of three 3D objects, constructed with the aid of **TABSURF** and **RULESURF** are shown in Fig. 3.19. Construct the three drawings. A problem arises when fitting **Rulesurf** surfaces on to **Tabsurf** extrusions. When the Pline outlines for the **Tabsurf** extrusions are drawn, they will be on the surface of the WCS x,y plane. When fitting the **Rulesurf** surface mesh, instead of it fitting on the top of the **Tabsurf** mesh as might be expected, it may fit at the bottom. The reader is advised to solve this problem without further help.

10. Figure 3.20 is a 3D drawing of a model formed with the aid of the 3D Object **BOX**. Following the order of work given, construct the drawing.

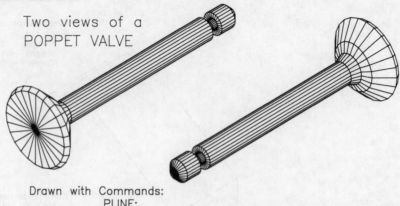

Two views of a
POPPET VALVE

Drawn with Commands:
          PLINE:
          REVSURF: Surftab1 set at 25
          ERASE: Erase Plin and Axis of Revolution
          COPY: Copy first Revsurf to obtain second
          ROTATE: Through 180
          VPOINT: −1,−1,1
          HIDE:

Fig. 3.18 Exercise 8

Commands used:
   PLINE:
   LINE:
   TABSURF: Surftab1 8
   RULESURF:
   MOVE:
   VPOINT:
   HIDE:

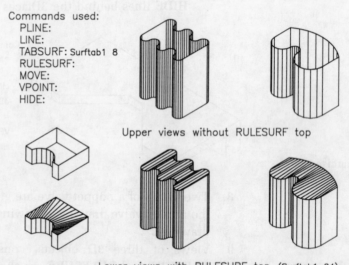

Upper views without RULESURF top

Fig. 3.19 Exercise 9   Lower views with RULESURF top (Surftab1 24)

11. A 3D drawing of a lathe headstock fitting is given in Fig. 3.21. Copy the drawing following the details included with Fig. 3.18.

12. Following the details of stages given in Fig. 3.22, construct the given 3D drawing.

13. Figure 3.23 is a 3D drawing of a handle for fitting to a braking device. It has been constructed from Surface meshes. Figure

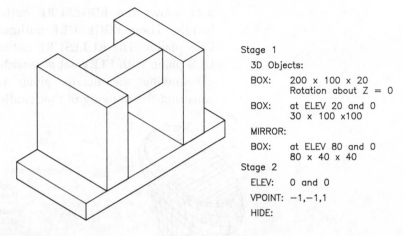

Fig. 3.20 Exercise 10

Stage 1
3D Objects:
BOX: 200 x 100 x 20
         Rotation about Z = 0
BOX: at ELEV 20 and 0
         30 x 100 x100
MIRROR:
BOX: at ELEV 80 and 0
         80 x 40 x 40
Stage 2
ELEV: 0 and 0
VPOINT: −1,−1,1
HIDE:

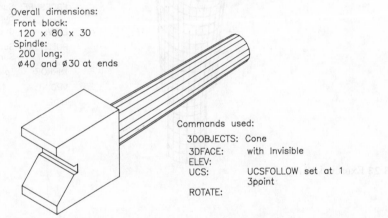

Fig. 3.21 Exercise 11

Overall dimensions:
Front block:
  120 x 80 x 30
Spindle:
  200 long;
  ∅40 and ∅30 at ends

Commands used:
  3DOBJECTS: Cone
  3DFACE: with Invisible
  ELEV:
  UCS: UCSFOLLOW set at 1
             3point
  ROTATE:

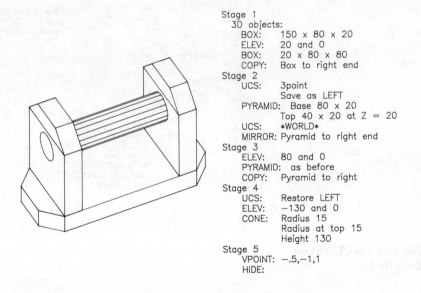

Fig. 3.22 Exercise 12

Stage 1
3D objects:
  BOX: 150 x 80 x 20
  ELEV: 20 and 0
  BOX: 20 x 80 x 80
  COPY: Box to right end
Stage 2
  UCS: 3point
           Save as LEFT
  PYRAMID: Base 80 x 20
           Top 40 x 20 at Z = 20
  UCS: *WORLD*
  MIRROR: Pyramid to right end
Stage 3
  ELEV: 80 and 0
  PYRAMID: as before
  COPY: Pyramid to right
Stage 4
  UCS: Restore LEFT
  ELEV: −130 and 0
  CONE: Radius 15
           Radius at top 15
           Height 130
Stage 5
  VPOINT: −.5,−1,1
  HIDE:

3.24 shows the **EDGESURF** outlines for the body of the handle. These **EDGESURF** outlines were drawn on several UCS planes. The **RULESURF** outlines were also drawn on a UCS plane with **ELEV** set at 0 with a thickness of 10.

Following the details given in the two illustrations, construct the drawing of the handle.

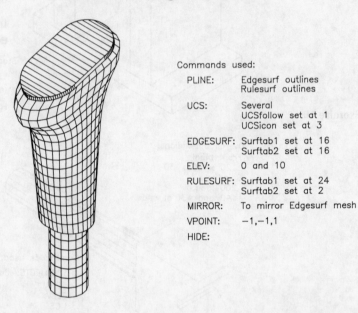

Commands used:

PLINE: Edgesurf outlines
           Rulesurf outlines

UCS: Several
           UCSfollow set at 1
           UCSicon set at 3

EDGESURF: Surftab1 set at 16
           Surftab2 set at 16

ELEV: 0 and 10

RULESURF: Surftab1 set at 24
           Surftab2 set at 2

MIRROR: To mirror Edgesurf mesh

VPOINT: −1,−1,1

HIDE:

Fig. 3.23 Exercise 13

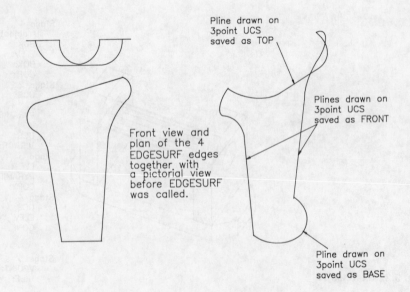

Pline drawn on
3point UCS
saved as TOP

Plines drawn on
3point UCS
saved as FRONT

Front view and
plan of the 4
EDGESURF edges
together with
a pictorial view
before EDGESURF
was called.

Pline drawn on
3point UCS
saved as BASE

Fig. 3.24 The **PLINE**s for
Exercise 13

14. Another braking device handle is shown in Fig. 3.25. This 3D drawing was constructed in a similar manner to the drawing given with Exercise 13.

Construct the handle working to the details given with Fig. 3.25.

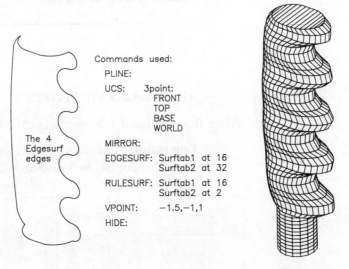

The 4 Edgesurf edges

Commands used:

PLINE:

UCS: 3point:
            FRONT
            TOP
            BASE
            WORLD

MIRROR:

EDGESURF: Surftab1 at 16
            Surftab2 at 32

RULESURF: Surftab1 at 16
            Surftab2 at 2

VPOINT: −1.5,−1,1

HIDE:

Fig. 3.25 Exercise 14

15. Figure 3.26 shows yet another 3D drawing of a braking handle. Construct the drawing, working to the same principles as with the two previous exercises.

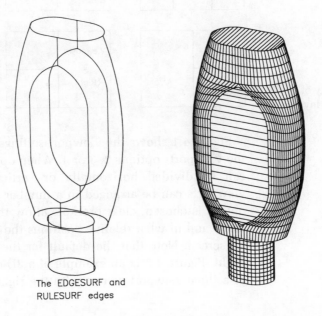

Fig. 3.26 Exercise 15

The EDGESURF and RULESURF edges

CHAPTER 4

Viewports, Tilemode, MSpace and PSpace

The command VIEWPORTS

When the command **Viewports** is called the command line shows:

Command: viewports *key Return*
Save/Restore/Delete/Join/Single/2/<3>/4:

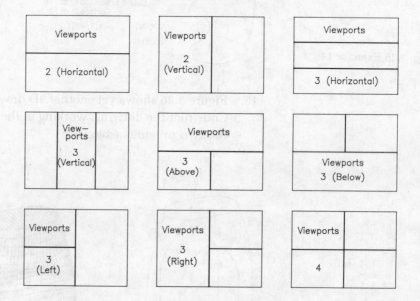

Fig. 4.1 The variety of possible viewport layouts

Figure 4.1 shows the viewport settings which are possible under the viewports options 2, 3 or 4. When option 2 is chosen the screen can be divided horizontally or vertically. With option 3, the viewports can be arranged in a number of ways. No matter which option is chosen, clear prompts allow the operator to choose how many and in what relative positions the viewports can be arranged on screen. Note that the default for the viewports option is **<3> Right**. Figure 4.2 is an example of a 3D drawing being constructed in a three-viewport screen with the right-hand viewport being the largest of the three. As a 3D model is constructed in the largest of the three viewports, changes are reflected in the other two. In this example the two smaller viewports are showing pictorial views from different viewpoints, thus any errors which may occur during construction will probably be identified in the two smaller pictorial views as the drawing is being created.

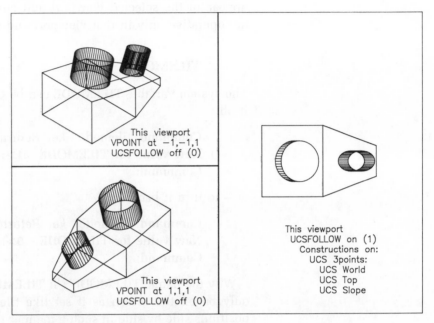

Fig. 4.2 A model under construction on a three viewport screen

UCSFOLLOW and VPOINT settings in VIEWPORTS

1. **UCSFOLLOW** can be set for each viewport – **ON** (1) in some and **OFF** (0) in others. Any UCS options will be followed in those viewports where **UCSFOLLOW** is **ON**;
2. **VPOINT** can be set separately for each viewport.

The settings of **UCSFOLLOW** and **VPOINT** in the example Fig. 4.2 were:

1. **UCSFOLLOW** – in largest viewport set to 1 (on); in the two smaller viewports set to 0 (off);
2. **VPOINT** – in upper, smaller viewport set to −1,−1,1; in lower, smaller viewport set to 1,1,1.

It is possible to have 16 viewports on screen – one of which is that which contains all others. This can be checked – call **VIEWPORTS**, select option 4 and *Fit*, call **VIEWPORTS** again and window four viewports in each quarter screen. The result will be that, in the last viewport in which one attempts to fit four viewports, only three will appear. This indicates that the first viewport is taken to be that which contains all others.

The current viewport – that in which construction is to take place – is chosen by pointing at the selected viewport and pressing the *pick* button of the pointing device. The cursor cross hairs then appear in the selected viewport and commands which are called are operative only in that viewport and not in others.

TILEMODE

The system variable **TILEMODE** can be **ON** (1) or **OFF** (0). To turn it off:

> **Command:** tilemode   *key Return*
> **New value for TILEMODE <1>:** 0   *key Return*
> **Command:**

or – to turn it back on:

> **Command:** tilemode   *key Return*
> **New value for TILEMODE <0>:** 1   *key Return*
> **Command:**

Why the name 'TILEMODE'? If **TILEMODE** is **ON**, viewports can only be on the screen as if set like tiles on a wall, i.e. in fixed positions side by side in such a manner that they cannot be moved from these set positions. When **TILEMODE** is **OFF**, each viewport can be moved to a new position relative to other viewports.

AutoCAD Release 10 compatibility with Release 11

When **TILEMODE** is **ON** (1), Release 11 of AutoCAD is compatible with Release 10.

Model Space and Paper Space

With the drawing editor set to Model Space (**MS**pace) constructions of either 2D or 3D drawings are possible. MSpace is available whether **TILEMODE** is **ON** or **OFF**.

With the drawing editor set to Paper Space (**PS**pace) 3D drawings cannot be constructed, but notes can be added to 3D drawings which have been constructed in Model Space (MSpace). While in **PS**pace, viewports can be rearranged for position and the plotting of as many viewports as are on screen. PSpace can only operate if **TILEMODE** is **OFF**.

With **TILEMODE** set **OFF**, **PS**pace can be changed to MSpace by:

> **Command:** ms (MSpace)   *key Return*
> **Command:**

and the screen changes to Model Space.

Similarly, with **TILEMODE** set **OFF**, to change back to **PS**pace:

> **Command:** ps (PSpace)   *key Return*
> **Command:**

and the screen reverts to Paper Space.

When a **NEW** drawing is called by selecting:

1. Begin a NEW drawing:

from the AutoCAD **Main Menu**, the default drawing file *acad.dwg* is loaded automatically from disk, unless AutoCAD has been configured (under **8. Configure AutoCAD** of the **Main Menu**) to load another drawing file.

The *acad.dwg* file sets a number of variables which control methods of drawing in the drawing editor. One of these variables is **TILEMODE**, which in the *acad.dwg* file is usually set **ON** (1).

When working with Release 11, a suggested method of constructing 3D drawings in the AutoCAD editor is:

1. Construct the required drawing in MSpace.
2. Set **TILEMODE** to **OFF** (0), which changes the screen to Paper Space (**PS**pace).
3. Make and set a new layer **VPorts** (or **VP**).
4. Set up the screen for the required number of viewports.
5. Add notes and rearrange viewports as necessary.
6. Plot from **PS**pace (all viewports on screen) when ready to do so. Plots can also be made from **MS**pace (but only of the current viewport).
7. If amendments are required in a 3D drawing, they can only be made after calling **MS**pace. This is because 3D drawing cannot proceed in **PS**pace. Note that even with **TILEMODE** set **OFF**, **MS**pace can still function.

Further notes about Model Space and Paper Space

1. In **PS**pace, the **PS**pace icon appears at the lower left-hand corner of the screen only if **UCSICON** is **ON**. If **UCSICON** is **OFF** the **PS**pace icon does not appear.
2. **VPOINT** is not available in **PS**pace. If **VPOINT** is called while

in **PS**pace a warning appears:

*** Command not allowed in Paper space ***

3. **UCSFOLLOW** is not operative in **PS**pace even when set **ON** (1). This means that a new UCS cannot be set when in **PS**pace.

4. Although new UCS systems cannot be constructed in **PS**pace, the UCS view currently in **MS**pace will remain when changing to **PS**pace from **MS**pace.

Viewports can be set up in either Model Space or Paper Space. However, when in **PS**pace the command **VIEWPORTS** is not allowed. In its place, a command **MVIEW** is available in **PS**pace for setting the required number of viewports.

When **PS**pace is first called (usually by setting **TILEMODE** to **OFF**) the screen becomes blank, except for the **PS**pace icon at the bottom left. Nothing can be added to the screen until one or more viewports are set by calling the command **MVIEW**:

> **Command:** mview   *key Return*
> **ON/OFF/Hideplot/Fit/2/3/4/Restore/<First Point>:** f (Fit)
> *key Return*
> **Command:**

and the screen changes to a single viewport occupying (fitting) the whole screen drawing area. Any drawing constructions from **MS**pace also appear on screen. If the response is either 2, 3 or 4, the

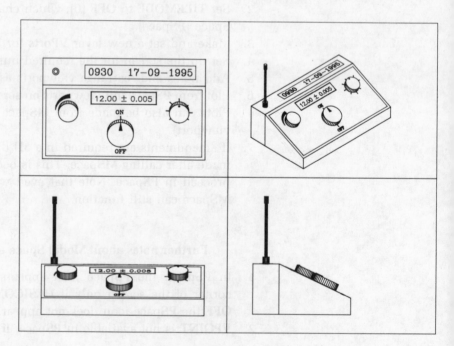

Fig. 4.3 A four-viewport drawing of a 3D model

screen changes to contain 2, 3 or 4 viewports. An example of a 4 viewport drawing is given in Fig. 4.3.

When in **PS**pace with several viewports, each viewport can be moved with the aid of the **MOVE** command, as can be seen in Fig. 4.4.

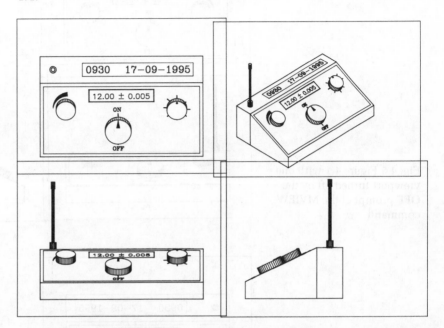

Fig. 4.4 Figure 4.1 with viewports **MOVED** to more suitable positions. Note viewport with the end view has been mirrored to obtain a sensible third angle projection of the end view.

The **MVIEW** prompts have the following meanings:

1. **OFF**: the contents of a viewport can be cleared by *picking* an edge of that viewport. The viewport then becomes blank. An example of a viewport turned off is given by Fig. 4.5.
2. **ON**: brings back on screen the contents of a viewport which has been turned **OFF**.
3. Hideplot: if an edge of a viewport is selected when **HIDEPLOT** is **ON**, hidden lines within that viewport will be removed when plotting.
   Note: Figs 4.4 to 4.13 have all been plotted with hidden lines removed by calling **Hideplot** from **MVIEW**, turning **HIDEPLOT ON** and then selecting the edge of each of the four viewports.
4. **Fit/2/3/4**: number of viewports required. If **FIT** then only a single viewport occupying the whole screen appears.
5. **R**estore: the contents of a viewport can be restored and fitted in a window of the operator's choice, by following the **Fit/<First point>**: and **Second point**: prompts. In Fig. 4.6 a **R**estored viewport has been displayed into a small window by selecting

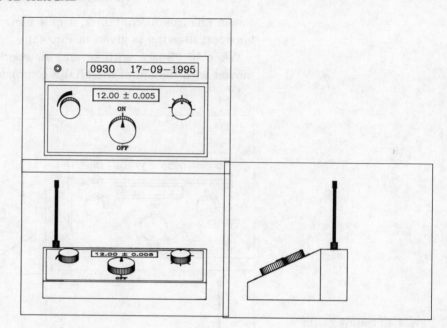

Fig. 4.5 Figure 4.1 with one viewport turned off by the **OFF** prompt of the **MVIEW** command

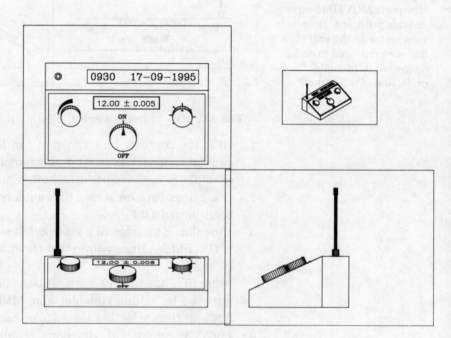

Fig. 4.6 Figure 4.3 with the viewport returned to screen in a window by the **Restore** prompt of the **MVIEW** command

the first and second points of the window corners.

6. **First point**: viewport(s) can be fitted into a window by selecting **First point:** and **Second point:**

Viewports in PSpace and MSpace

1. When in **PS**pace, viewports can be turned off or on, moved, scaled or copied. An edge of the viewport to be acted upon by the commands move, copy, scale or erase is *picked* for the required changes to occur within that viewport;

2. When in **MS**pace, the viewing position for 3D model drawings can be set in each viewport independently with the aid of the **VPOINT** command (Fig. 4.7). Remember **VPOINT** is not available when in **PS**pace, but the **VPOINT** views set in **MS**pace are retained when switching to **PS**pace.

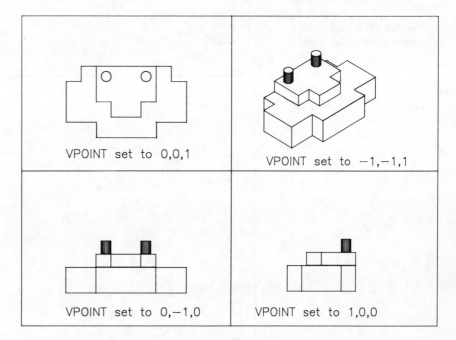

Fig. 4.7 A 3D model with each viewport showing a different **VPOINT** view

Setting viewports in Paper Space

The following procedure for setting viewports in Paper Space is intended to allow a plot of a 3D drawing to obtain a three-view orthographic projection, together with a pictorial view. The drawing has been constructed on a screen set to limits 420,300 (for a full-sized-plot on an A3 sheet).

1. Construct the drawing in **MS**pace (Fig. 4.8).
2. Set **TILEMODE** to 0 (**OFF**). This sets up **PS**pace (Fig. 4.9).
3. Set Limits to 0,0 and 420,297 (A3 sheet millimetre sizes).
4. Zoom all. Set screen to limits 400,297.
5. Make a new layer Vport, colour yellow.

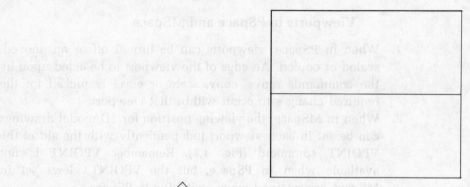

Fig. 4.8 3D model constructed in **MS**pace

Fig. 4.9 The screen changed to **PS**pace. The drawing disappears

6. Make layer Vport current.
7. Call **MVIEW** to obtain four viewports, fitted to the screen (Fig. 4.10).
8. Call **MS**pace.
9. Call **VPOINT** in each viewport in turn (point to viewport and *pick*) and set viewing positions:
    (a) Top left viewport 0,0,1;
    (b) Bottom left viewport 0,−1,0;

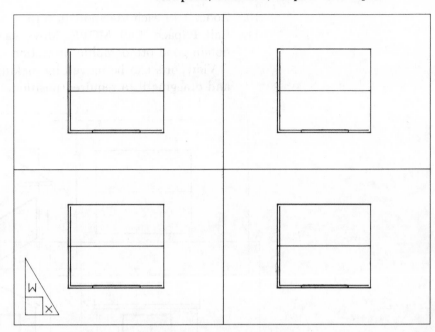

Fig. 4.10 In **MVIEW** – four viewports. Fitted to screen editor. The drawing reappears

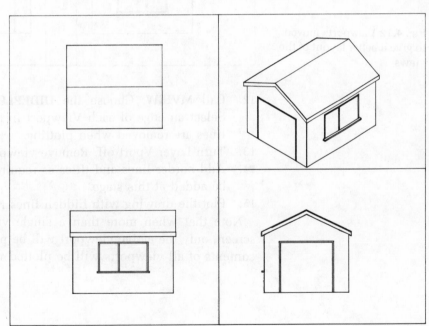

Fig. 4.11 Four viewports rearranged with **VPOiNT** to obtain orthographic views and a pictorial view

(c) Bottom right viewport 1,0,0;

(d) Top right viewport −1,−1,1.

The results of these various Vpoint settings are shown in Fig. 4.11.

10. Zoom 1 in each viewport in turn.
11. Call **PS**pace. Call **MOVE**. Move each viewport in turn to obtain good orthographic projection of the views (Fig. 4.12).

Viewports can be moved by *picking* an edge of a viewport and dragging it to required position.

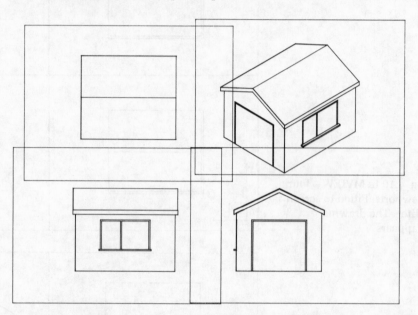

Fig. 4.12 Viewports moved to give a better layout of the views

12. Call **MVIEW**. Choose the **HIDEPLOT** prompt. Set to **ON**. Select an edge of each Viewport in turn. Ensure that hidden lines are removed when plotting.
13. Turn Layer Vport **off**. Remove viewport lines.
14. Add border lines and titles as required. Dimensions can also be added at this stage.
15. Plot the drawing with hidden lines removed (Fig. 4.13).

Note that when more than a single viewport is displayed on screen, only the active viewport will be plotted if in **MS**pace. The contents of all viewports will be plotted when in **PS**pace.

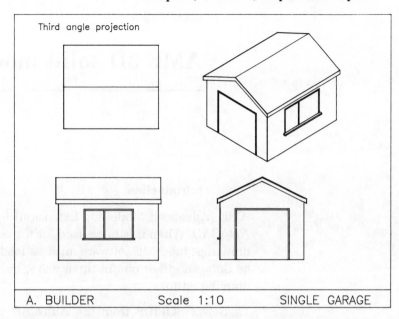

Third angle projection

A. BUILDER   Scale 1:10   SINGLE GARAGE

Fig. 4.13 Viewport layer
turned off. Border and title
added

CHAPTER 5

AME 3D solid model drawings

Introduction

AME (Advanced Modelling Extension) is an extension program to
AutoCAD. When it is to be used for the construction of solid model
drawings, the AME software must be loaded into memory. This can
be done in either one of three ways, once one is in the AutoCAD
drawing editor.

1. Select **SOLIDS** from the AutoCAD main on-screen area. The
   menu changes to a sub-menu containing the commands **LOAD
   AME** and **LOAD AMELITE**. Point at **LOAD AME** and the AME
   software loads into memory;
2. Select **SOLIDS** from the pull-down menu names at the Status
   line. The pull-down menu shows the two commands **Load
   AME** and **Load AMElite**. Point at **Load AME** and the AME
   software loads into memory; or
3. At the keyboard enter (XLoad"AME"). The AME software then
   loads into memory.

Note the command **LOAD AMElite**. Within the AutoCAD
Release 11 software is a sub-set of the AME commands. Although
full solid model drawing cannot be constructed with the AMElite
set, items such as the AME solid primitives can be brought to
screen through AMElite without the optional AME extension
software being available.

The AME command set

All commands from the Advanced Modelling Extension begin with
SOL (solid). Once the AME software has been loaded, these
commands can be selected from:

1. The **SOLIDS** on-screen menus, which brings up sub-menus
   from which the **SOL** commands can be selected;
2. The pull-down **Sol-Prim's** pull-down menu, with its sub-
   menus;

3. From the ADVANCED MODELLING area of the standard AutoCAD Release 11 tablet overlay;
4. By entering either the full or the abbreviated **SOL** commands at the keyboard.

In this chapter all AME commands will be shown as entered in full at the keyboard.

The acad.pgp file

Reference has already been made to the *acad.pgp* file (Chapter 1, page 4), in which command name abbreviations are determined. Most of the AME commands are included in the abbreviations listed in this file. Hence nearly all of the AME commands can be called by entering an abbreviation at the keyboard. The following is extracted from the *acad.pgp* file included with the standard AutoCAD Release 11 disks. The AME command name abbreviations included in *acad.pgp* are given below as seen in the file:

; These are the local aliases for AutoCAD AME commands.
; **Comment** out any you don't want or add your own.
; Note that aliases must be typed completely.

Primitives

BOX,	*SOLBOX
WED,	*SOLWEDGE
WEDGE,	*SOLWEDGE
CON,	*SOLCONE
CONE,	*SOLCONE
CYL,	*SOLCYLINDER
CYLINDER,	*SOLCYLINDER
SPH,	*SOLSPHERE
SPHERE,	*SOLSPHERE
TOR,	*SOLTORUS
TORUS,	*SOLTORUS

Complex Solids

fiL,	*SOLfiLL
SOLF	*SOLfiLL
CHAM,	*SOLCHAM
SOLC,	*SOLCHAM
EXT,	*SOLEXT
EXTRUDE,	*SOLEXT
SUB,	*SOLSUB
SUBTRACT,	*SOLSUB
DIF,	*SOLSUB

DIFFERENCE,	*SOLSUB
SEP,	*SOLSEP
SEPARATE,	*SOLSEP

Modification and Query commands

SCHP,	*SOLCHP
CHPRIM,	*SOLCHP
MAT,	*SOLMAT
MATERIAL,	*SOLMAT
MOV	*SOLMOVE
SL,	*SOLLIST
SLIST,	*SOLLIST
MP,	*SOLMASSP
MASSP,	*SOLMASSP
SA,	*SOLAREA
SAAREA,	*SOLAREA
SSV,	*SOLVAR

Documentation commands

FEAT,	*SOLFEAT
PROF,	*SOLPROF
PROfiLE,	*SOLPROF
SU,	*SOLUCS
SUCS,	*SOLUCS

Model representation commands

SW,	*SOLWIRE
WIRE,	*SOLWIRE
SM,	*SOLMESH
MESH,	*SOLMESH

The AME primitives

There are six basic solid drawings in the AME set of Primitives.
These are shown in Fig. 5.1:

1. **SOLBOX**   for rectangular prisms or cubes;
2. **SOLCYL**   for either circular or elliptical cylinders;
3. **SOLCONE**   for either circular or elliptical cones;
4. **SOLSPHERE**   for spheres;
5. **SOLTORUS**   (a closed torus can be drawn if the tube radius is larger than the torus radius);
6. **SOLWEDGE**   for wedge-shaped 3D solid drawings.

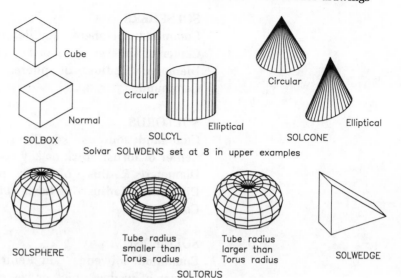

Fig. 5.1 The primitive **SOL**ids in the AME set

Prompts and options for the primitives

SOLBOX
Command: solbox   *key Return*
Corner of box: *pick* or *key* coordinates
Cube/Length/<Other corner>:   *pick* or c (Cube) or *l*

(Length)

Height: *key* a figure *Return*
Command:

SOLCONE
Command: solcone   *key Return*
Elliptical/<Center point>:   *pick* or e (Elliptical)
Diameter/<Radius>:   *pick* or *key* coordinates *Return*
Height of cone: *key* a figure *Return*
Command:

SOLCYLINDER

Command: solcyl   *key Return*
Elliptical/<Center point>:   *pick* or e (Elliptical)
Diameter/<Radius>:   *pick* or *key* coordinates *Return*
Height of cylinder: *key* a figure *Return*
Command:

SOLSPHERE
Command: solsphere   *key Return*
Center of sphere: *pick or key coordinates Return*
Diameter/<Radius> of sphere: *pick or key a number*
Command:

SOLTORUS
Command: soltorus   *key Return*
Center of torus: *pick or key coordinates*
Diameter/<Radius> of torus: *pick or key a number*
Diameter/<Radius> of tube: *pick or key a number*
Command:

SOLWEDGE
Command: solwedge   *key Return*
Corner of wedge: *pick or key coordinates*
Length/<Other corner>:   *pick or key coordinates*
Height: *Key a figure Return*
Command:

During the pauses which occur between the stages in the construction of a primitive, various statements may appear at the command line, informing the operator as to what is happening while waiting for the construction to complete.

Wireframes and surface meshes

Solid models produced with the aid of AME appear on screen as wireframes, behind which lines cannot be hidden by calling the command **HIDE**. The wireframes can be changed to surface meshes by calling the command **SOLMESH** and *picking* the solid model drawing which one wishes to surface mesh. When an AME 3D model drawing is acted upon by **SOLMESH**, hidden lines behind faces will be hidden by the **HIDE** command.

Command: solmesh   *key Return*
Select objects to be meshed . . .
Select objects: *pick* **1 selected, 1 found**
Select objects: *Return*
1 solid selected
Command:

During the pauses between the prompts, a variety of messages will appear at the command line informing the operator of what is happening during the pauses.

The AME variable SOLWDENS

The density of the mesh of those primitives which incorporate curved lines is controlled by the **SOLVAR** (solid variable) **SOLWDENS** (solid wire density). **SOLWDENS** can be set between 1 and 8, the higher the number the closer the density of the mesh. Note also that each mesh in the primitives containing curved parts is a PFACE with straight edges. Thus the greater the density of the mesh, the closer to accuracy will the primitive's curves be. However, close density means that the drawing file for an AME 3D model will become larger. To change the variable enter **SOLWDENS** at the keyboard. When the prompt appears enter the desired density figure (up to 8).

The AME command SOLEXT

2D outlines composed from plines, circles, ellipses or polygons can be extruded with the aid of the AME command **SOLEXT**. Such extrusions can become surface meshed with the aid of **SOLMESH**. figure 5.2 gives examples of a variety of extrusions from 2D outlines. Note that if the 2D outline is open, it is automatically closed when acted upon by **SOLEXT**.

The AME command SOLREV

Solids of revolution can be formed with the aid of the command **SOLREV**. The prompts and options are:

> **Command:** solrev   *key Return*
> **Select polyline or circle for revolution . . .**
> **Select objects:**   *pick* **1 selected, 1 found**
> **Select objects:**   *Return*
> **Axis of revolution – Entity/X/Y/<Start point of axis>:**
>
> $\qquad\qquad\qquad\qquad\qquad\qquad\qquad\qquad\qquad\qquad$ *pick*
>
> **End point of axis:**   *pick*
> **Included angle <full circle>:**   *Return*
> **Command:**

Figure 5.2 shows a number of solids of revolution formed with the aid of this command. Note there is no need to draw an axis of revolution. It is only necessary to *pick* or *key* the coordinates of the ends. The axes are centre lines in Fig. 5.3 to show the reader where the axes lie in relation to the plines from which the solids of revolution are generated.

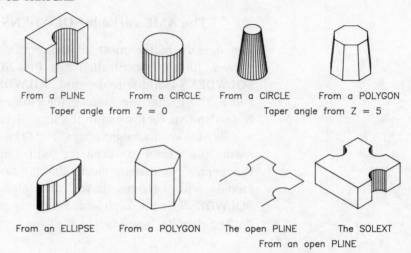

From a PLINE   From a CIRCLE   From a CIRCLE   From a POLYGON
Taper angle from Z = 0   Taper angle from Z = 5

From an ELLIPSE   From a POLYGON   The open PLINE   The SOLEXT
From an open PLINE

Fig. 5.2 Examples of SOLEXT extrusions from plines, circle, ellipse and polygon lines

If a circle is chosen as the circle of revolution, a torus will be formed. If the **e** (Entity) option is selected, the revolution will take place around a pline or line *picked* from any on the screen. Polylines or circles can also be revolved around their own x- or y-axes by choosing either of these two options.

Partial solids of revolution can be formed by entering a figure for an angle in response to the **Included angle <full circle>:** prompt. Examples are shown in Fig. 5.4.

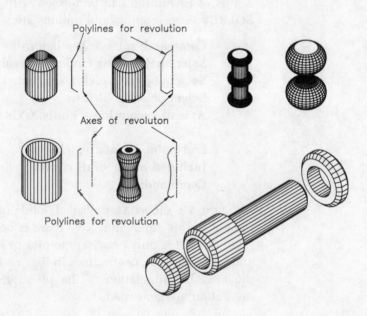

Polylines for revolution

Axes of revoluton

Polylines for revolution

Fig. 5.3 Examples of full circle SOLREV solids of revolution

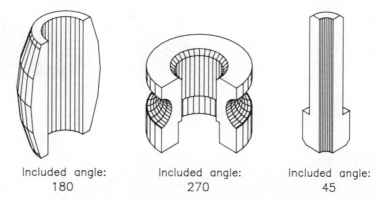

Fig. 5.4 Examples of
included angle **SOLREV**
solids of revolution

Included angle:
180

Included angle:
270

Included angle:
45

The Boolean operators

AME primitives and those formed by **SOLEXT** and **SOLREV** can be joined, subtracted from and intersected with each other. The commands for these operations are **SOLUNION**, **SOLSUB** and **SOLINT**. These produce the Boolean operations union, difference and intersection.

The AME command SOLUNION

Figure 5.5 shows three solids, each formed from two primitives, by the action of the AME command **SOLUNION**. When **SOLUNION** is called, the command line of the drawing editor shows a series of statements as the primitives are acted upon by the command:

> **Command:** solunion   *key Return*
> **Select objects:**   *pick* **1 selected, 1 found**
> **Select objects:**   *pick* **1 selected, 1 found**
> **Select objects:**   *Return*
> **2 objects selected.**
> **Phase 1 – Boundary evaluation begins.**
> **3 of 20 of Phase I in progress.**
> **Phase II – Tesselation computation begins.**
> **Updating the Advanced Modelling Extension database.**
> **Command:**

The upper three drawings of Fig. 5.5 show primitives before calling the command **SOLUNION**. The lower three show the same drawings as solid model drawings after the action of **SOLUNION** and **SOLMESH**.

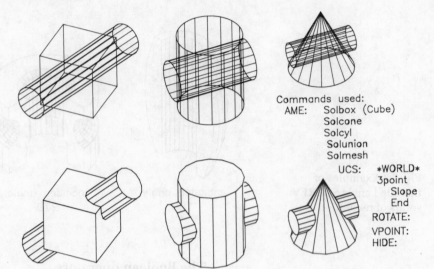

Commands used:
AME: Solbox (Cube)
        Solcone
        Solcyl
        Solunion
        Solmesh

UCS: *WORLD*
        3point
        Slope
        End
ROTATE:
VPOINT:
HIDE:

Fig. 5.5 Examples of the
results of **SOLUNION**

The AME command SOLSUB

Figure 5.6 shows three solids, each formed from two primitives, by
the action of the AME command **SOLSUB**. When the command is
called, the command line shows a series of statements as the
primitives are subtracted one from the other:

Command: solsub   key Return
Source objects . . .
Select objects: pick **1 selected, 1 found**
Select objects: Return
1 solid selected.
Objects to subtract from them . . .
Select objects: pick **1 selected, 1 found**
Select objects: Return
1 object selected.
Phase I – Boundary evaluation begins.
3 of 20 of Phase I in progress.
Phase II – Tesselation computation begins.
Updating the Advanced Modelling Extension database.
Command:

The upper three drawings of Fig. 5.6 show primitives before
calling the command **SOLSUB**. The lower three show the same
drawings as solid model drawings after the action of **SOLSUB** and
SOLMESH.

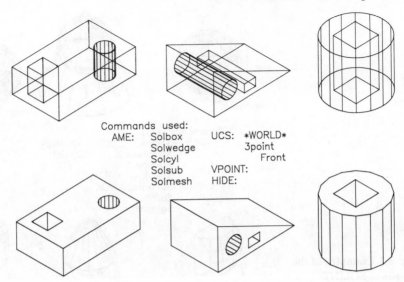

Commands used:
AME: Solbox   UCS: *WORLD*
        Solwedge   3point
        Solcyl   Front
        Solsub   VPOINT:
        Solmesh   HIDE:

Fig. 5.6 Examples of the
results of **SOLSUB**

The AME command SOLINT

Figure 5.7 shows three solids, each formed from two primitives, by
the action of the AME command **SOLINT**. When the command is
called, the command line shows a series of statements as the
primitives are subtracted one from the other:

> **Command:** solint   *key Return*
> **Select objects:**   *pick* **1 selected, 1 found**
> **Select objects:**   *pick* **1 selected, 1 found**
> **Select objects:**   *Return*
> **2 solids selected.**
> **Phase I – Boundary evaluation begins.**
> **3 of 20 of Phase I in progress.**
> **Phase II – Tesselation computation begins.**
> **Updating the Advanced Modelling Extension database.**
> **Command:**

The upper three drawings of Fig. 5.7 show primitives before
calling the command **SOLINT**. The lower three show the same
drawings as solid model drawings after the action of **SOLINT** and
SOLMESH.

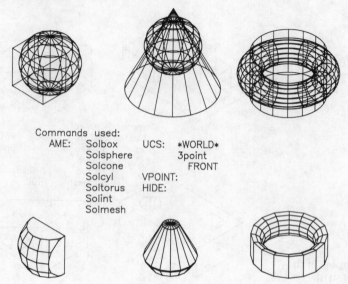

Commands used:
AME: Solbox   UCS: *WORLD*
        Solsphere   3point
        Solcone   FRONT
        Solcyl   VPOINT:
        Soltorus   HIDE:
        Solint
        Solmesh

Fig. 5.7 Examples of the
results of **SOLINT**

Examples of SOLUNION and SOLSUB

Figures 5.8 to 5.12 are examples 3D model drawings formed from primitives, extrusions and solids of revolution with the aid of these two AME commands. Details of the commands employed are included, together with main dimensions for the benefit of those who wish to construct these examples. Use your own judgement for those sizes which are not included.

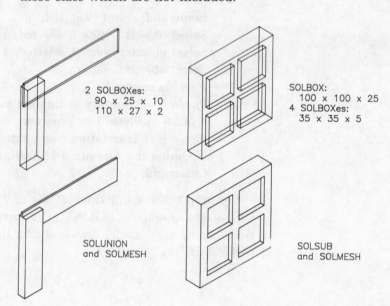

2 SOLBOXes:
90 x 25 x 10
110 x 27 x 2

SOLBOX:
100 x 100 x 25
4 SOLBOXes:
35 x 35 x 5

SOLUNION
and SOLMESH

SOLSUB
and SOLMESH

Fig. 5.8 Two examples of
simple AME solids using
SOLUNION and **SOLSUB**

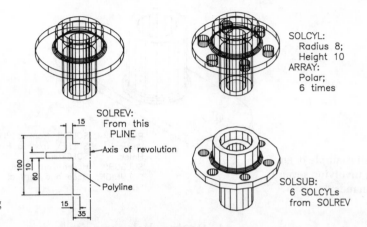

SOLCYL:
Radius 8;
Height 10
ARRAY:
Polar;
6 times

SOLREV:
From this
PLINE

Axis of revolution

Polyline

SOLSUB:
6 SOLCYLs
from SOLREV

Fig. 5.9 Stages in constructing
an AME solid with **SOLREV**

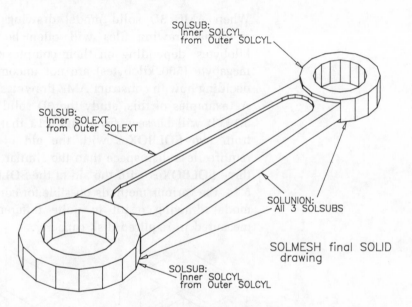

SOLSUB:
Inner SOLCYL
from Outer SOLCYL

SOLSUB:
Inner SOLEXT
from Outer SOLEXT

SOLUNION:
All 3 SOLSUBS

SOLMESH final SOLID
drawing

SOLSUB:
Inner SOLCYL
from Outer SOLCYL

Fig. 5.10 An example of an
AME solid involving several
AME commands

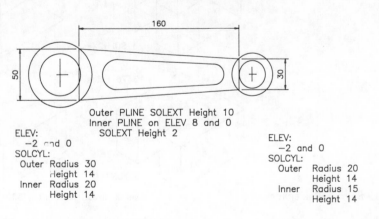

160

50

30

Outer PLINE SOLEXT Height 10
Inner PLINE on ELEV 8 and 0
SOLEXT Height 2

ELEV:
−2 and 0
SOLCYL:
Outer Radius 30
Height 14
Inner Radius 20
Height 14

ELEV:
−2 and 0
SOLCYL:
Outer Radius 20
Height 14
Inner Radius 15
Height 14

Fig. 5.11 Dimensions for
constructing Fig. 5.10

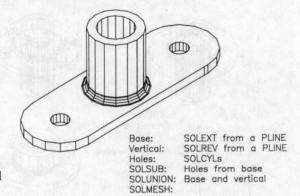

Fig. 5.12 An example of an
AME solid involving several
AME commands

Base:	SOLEXT from a PLINE
Vertical:	SOLREV from a PLINE
Holes:	SOLCYLs
SOLSUB:	Holes from base
SOLUNION:	Base and vertical
SOLMESH:	

Saving disk capacity

When AME 3D solid model drawings are saved to disk, the
resulting drawing files will often be large, containing many
kilobytes, depending on their complexity. files in excess of 0.5
megabyte (500 kilobytes) are not uncommon. If care is taken in
deciding how to construct AME drawings, disk space can be saved.
As examples of this, study the 3D solid models in Figs 5.13 and
5.14. It will be seen from Fig. 5.13 that the 3D model produced
from two **SOLBOX**es with the aid of the **SOLSUB** command
requires less disk space than the similar 3D model produced from
three **SOLBOX**es with the aid of the **SOLUNION** command. In Fig.
5.14, the various methods possible for constructing the required 3D
model drawing result in quite different drawing file sizes as
measured in required disk capacity.

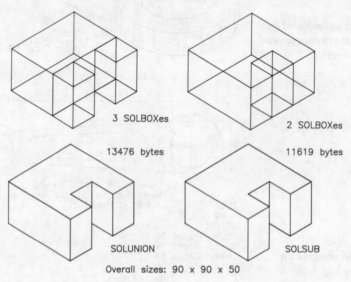

Fig. 5.13 Saving disk space

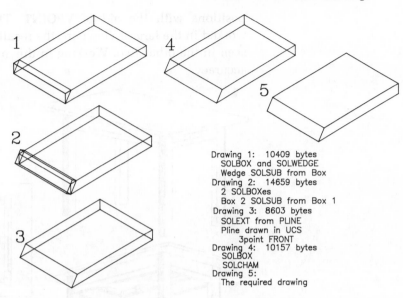

Drawing 1:   10409 bytes
  SOLBOX and SOLWEDGE
  Wedge SOLSUB from Box
Drawing 2:   14659 bytes
  2 SOLBOXes
  Box 2 SOLSUB from Box 1
Drawing 3:   8603 bytes
  SOLEXT from PLINE
  Pline drawn in UCS
        3point FRONT
Drawing 4:   10157 bytes
  SOLBOX
  SOLCHAM
Drawing 5:
  The required drawing

Fig. 5.14 Saving disk space

Primitive, extrusion or revolved solid?

Similar 3D model drawings can be constructed from primitives, extrusions or revolved models. An example of this is shown in Fig. 5.15.

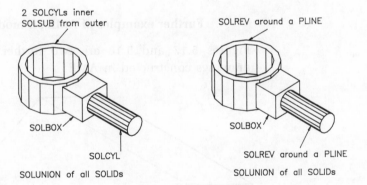

Fig. 5.15 Two methods of constructing an AME solid using different AME commands

Constructing 3D models in viewports

The method of constructing 3D model drawings which is probably that most frequently employed is to work in a three-viewport set-up such as shown in Fig. 5.16. The model can be constructed in the larger of the three viewports in the ***WORLD*** UCS (or any other UCS thought to be suitable). **UCSFOLLOW** must be at 0 (**OFF**) in the other two viewports, which are set to different viewing positions with the aid of **VPOINT**. Then, as constructions are worked in the largest viewport, the results in pictorial views can be seen in the other two. Working in this manner assists in achieving accuracy.

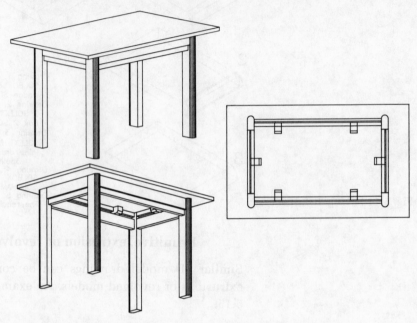

Fig. 5.16 The value of a three-viewport setting when constructing AME solids

Further examples of AME 3D model drawings

Figures 5.17 and 5.18 are two further examples of 3D model drawings constructed in AME.

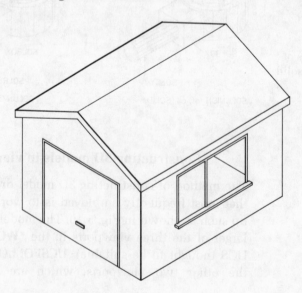

Fig. 5.17 A **VPOINT** view of an AME solid

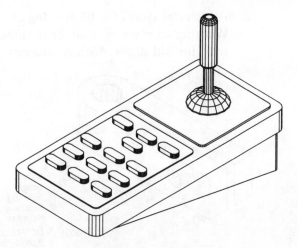

Fig. 5.18 An AME solid
drawing of a joystick

Exercises

Five exercises are given below to allow the reader to practise
constructing with the aid of the AME set of commands described in
this chapter. No dimensions are included with the drawings. Work
to convenient sizes.

1. Two views of a 3D drawing of a simple sawing board are given
   in Fig. 5.19. Construct the 3D drawing with the aid of the
   commands shown.

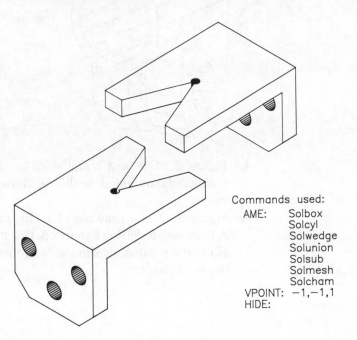

Commands used:
AME: Solbox
Solcyl
Solwedge
Solunion
Solsub
Solmesh
Solcham
VPOINT: −1,−1,1
HIDE:

Fig. 5.19 Two views of an
AME 3D solid model
drawing Exercise 1

2. A pictorial view of a 3D drawing of a clip is given in Fig. 5.20. Working to sizes of your own choice, construct the drawing with the aid of the AME commands shown.

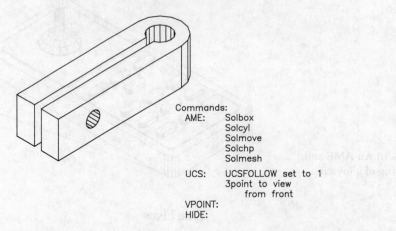

Commands:
AME: Solbox
          Solcyl
          Solmove
          Solchp
          Solmesh

UCS: UCSFOLLOW set to 1
          3point to view
                    from front

VPOINT:
HIDE:

Fig. 5.20 Exercise 2

3. Figure 5.21 is a **VPOINT** view of a pipe clip drawn with the aid of AME. Construct the drawing using suitable dimensions.

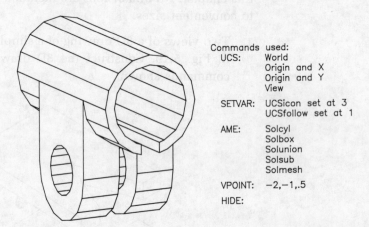

Commands used:
UCS: World
          Origin and X
          Origin and Y
          View

SETVAR: UCSicon set at 3
          UCSfollow set at 1

AME: Solcyl
          Solbox
          Solunion
          Solsub
          Solmesh

VPOINT: −2,−1,.5

HIDE:

Fig. 5.21 Exercise 3

4. Figure 5.22 is a 3D model of a clip. With the aid of the commands included with the drawing, construct the given model.

5. Figure 5.23 is a drawing of a clip drawn with the aid of the Advanced Modelling Extension. Construct the drawing with the aid of the commands shown. Note that **SOLFILL** is described in the next chapter.

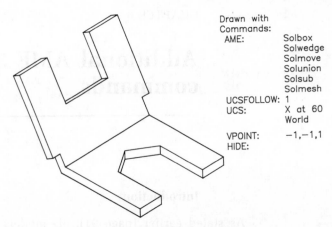

Drawn with
Commands:
AME:	Solbox
	Solwedge
	Solmove
	Solunion
	Solsub
	Solmesh
UCSFOLLOW:	1
UCS:	X at 60
	World
VPOINT:	−1,−1,1
HIDE:	

Fig. 5.22 Exercise 4

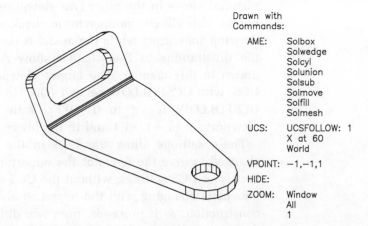

Drawn with
Commands:
AME:	Solbox
	Solwedge
	Solcyl
	Solunion
	Solsub
	Solmove
	Solfill
	Solmesh
UCS:	UCSFOLLOW: 1
	X at 60
	World
VPOINT:	−1,−1,1
HIDE:	
ZOOM:	Window
	All
	1

Fig. 5.23 Exercise 5

CHAPTER 6

Additional AME 3D model commands

Introduction

As stated earlier (page 91), 3D models are best constructed in a three-viewport screen. As the construction proceeds in the largest viewport, details of the construction can be made to appear as pictorial views in the other two viewports from different viewing points. This allows the operator to check whether details of the 3D drawing are correct while the model is being constructed. Some of the illustrations in this chapter show AME solids which were drawn in this manner. The largest viewport is in the ***WORLD*** UCS, with **UCSFOLLOW** set at 1 (**ON**). In the other two viewports **UCSFOLLOW** is set to 0 (**OFF**), with **VPOINT** in the upper viewport set to −1,−1,1 and in the lower viewport set to 1,−1,1.

These settings allow the UCS in the largest viewport to be changed to give the operator the opportunity to add details on a variety of UCS settings, without the UCS settings in the other two viewports changing with the largest. It also allows viewing of the construction, as it proceeds, from two different viewing points in the two smaller viewports.

The AME command SOLCHAM

A chamfer is formed on an AME 3D model by picking an edge of a correctly chosen surface of the model. The required surface, edge and the chamfer sizes are determined by the responses to the sequences of prompts and options appearing when **SOLCHAM** is called:

> **Command:** solcham   *key Return*
> **Select base surface:**   *pick an edge of the required surface*
> **<OK>/Next:**   *Return* (if selected surface is correct)
> > if not *key n (Next) Return*
> **Select edges to be chamfered (Press ENTER when done):**
> > *pick Return*

1 edge selected.
Enter distance along first surface <0>: 10 *key Return*
Enter distance along second surface <0>: 10 *key Return*
Phase I – Boundary evaluation begins.
3 of 15 of Phase I in process.
Phase II – Tesselation computation begins.
2 of 5 of Phase II in process.
Updating the Advanced Modelling Extension database.
Command:

Examples of chamfers formed on AME models with the aid of **SOLCHAM** are given in Fig. 6.1.

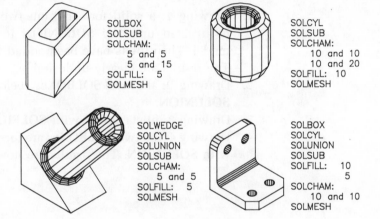

SOLBOX
SOLSUB
SOLCHAM:
    5 and 5
    5 and 15
SOLFILL: 5
SOLMESH

SOLCYL
SOLSUB
SOLCHAM:
    10 and 10
    10 and 20
SOLFILL: 10
SOLMESH

SOLWEDGE
SOLCYL
SOLUNION
SOLSUB
SOLCHAM:
    5 and 5
SOLFILL: 5
SOLMESH

SOLBOX
SOLCYL
SOLUNION
SOLSUB
SOLFILL: 10
          5
SOLCHAM:
    10 and 10
SOLMESH

Fig. 6.1 Examples of AME solids modified by **SOLCHAM** and **SOLFILL**

The AME command SOLFILL

The prompts, options and responses for **SOLFILL** are similar to those for **SOLCHAM**, except that only edges need to be picked and only one size (radius or diameter) is required for the command to commence functioning.

Command: solfill   *key Return*
Select edges to be filleted (Press ENTER when done):   *pick*
                                            Return

1 edge selected.
Diameter/<Radius> of fillet<0>: 5 *key Return*
Phase I – Boundary evaluation begins.
3 of 15 of Phase I in process.
Phase II – Tesselation computation begins.
2 of 5 of Phase II in process.

Updating the Advanced Modelling Extension database. Command:

Examples of fillets formed on AME models with the aid of **SOLFILL** are given in Fig. 6.1.

Problems arising with SOLFILL and SOLCHAM

Each AME fillet and chamfer included in 3D solid model is a separate 3D entity (a sub-model). This can give rise to undesirable results. An example of such a result arising from using **SOLFILL** is shown in Fig. 6.2, together with a method of overcoming the particular problem:

1. Drawing 1: a solid formed from two **SOLBOX**es which have been acted upon by **SOLUNION** to form a single 3D solid model. Then fillets have been added with the aid of **SOLFILL**. The results are clearly undesirable;
2. Drawing 2: the two **SOLBOX**es, before being combined with **SOLUNION**;
3. Drawing 3: fillets added with **SOLFILL**;
4. Drawing 4: the two **SOLBOX**es are formed into a single 3D solid with **SOLUNION**. The results are now as desired.

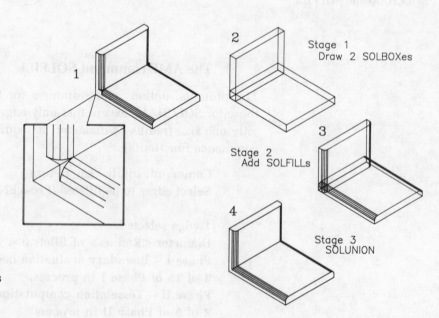

Stage 1
Draw 2 SOLBOXes

Stage 2
Add SOLFILLs

Stage 3
SOLUNION

Fig. 6.2 A possible error when using **SOLFILL** and its remedy

An example of an undesirable result arising from the use of **SOLCHAM** is given in Fig. 6.3, together with a method of overcoming the particular problem.

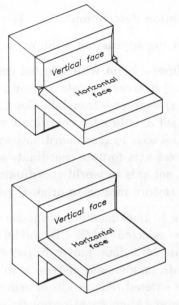

AME 3D solid model drawing formed from 2 SOLBOXes acted upon by SOLUNION

Horizontal faces chamfered with SOLCHAM before vertical faces

The same 3D solid model drawing with vertical edges chamfered with SOLCHAM before horizontal faces

Fig. 6.3 A possible error when using **SOLCHAM** and its remedy

From these two examples, it can be seen that some care is required when adding chamfers or fillets to AME 3D solid models with **SOLCHAM** or **SOLFILL**.

The AME command SOLMOVE

SOLMOVE is an AME command system which enables the user:

1. To move an AME 3D solid model in the direction of any of the three coordinate axes;
2. To rotate an AME 3D solid model around any of the three coordinate axes;
3. To align an AME 3D solid model with an edge or a face of another 3D model; and
4. To align an AME 3D solid model with an existing UCS.

When the command is called, the command line shows:

> **Command:** solmove   *key Return*
> Select objects: *pick* the required AME 3D drawing
> **1 solid selected.**
> **Redefining block SOLAXES**
> **<Motion description>/?:**

When the **SOLAXES** are redefined, the Motion Coordinate System (MCS) icon appears at the UCS origin (0,0,0). The motion description can be defined in any of several ways as is shown when ? is entered in response to the option:

<Motion description>/?:   *? key Return*

The following appears on a flipped text screen:

a[efuw] – align with selected coordinate system
r[xyz] degrees – rotate around selected axis
t[xyz] degrees – translate along selected axis
e – set axis to edge coordinate system
f – set axis to face coordinate system
u – set axis to user coordinate system
w – set axis to world coordinate system
o – restore motion to original position

According to the operator's response to the motion description option, the selected AME 3D model can be manipulated as required. The **MCS** icon moves to the edge or face picked on the selected AME model and moves with the model as movement prompts are entered. The results of using the **r** (**R**otate) prompt and of using the **af** (**A**lign **F**ace) responses are shown in Figs 6.4 and 6.5. The operator will probably find that the movement options most frequently required will be **t** (**T**ranslate) and the **r** (**R**otate) to

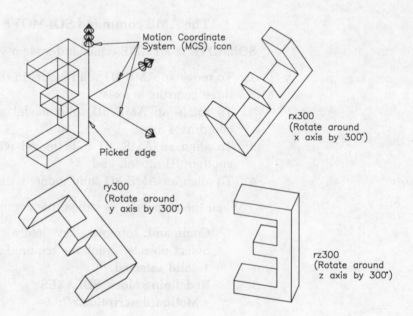

Fig. 6.4 Examples of moving an AME solid with the **SOLMOVE** options **e** (**E**dge) and **r** (**R**otate)

move or rotate an AME 3D drawing to new positions. Note that it is usually advisable to move (translate) or rotate a 3D model after the **SOLAXES** have been transferred to an edge or a face, although it is possible to move or rotate around the **SOLAXES** situated at the UCS origin. If movement is based on the **SOLAXES** at the origin, the results may not be as expected.

Note about the MCS

The **MCS** icon for the **SOLAXES** aligns itself with the 3D coordinate axes. The number of cones at the ends of the lines representing the three axes show which is the x- (one cone), which is the y- (two cones) and which is the z-axis (three cones).

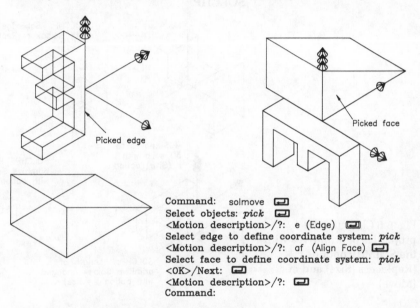

Fig. 6.5 Examples of moving an AME solid with the **SOLMOVE** options **e** (Edge) and **f** (Align Face)

```
Command:  solmove ⏎
Select objects: pick ⏎
<Motion description>/?:  e (Edge)  ⏎
Select edge to define coordinate system: pick
<Motion description>/?:  af (Align Face)  ⏎
Select face to define coordinate system: pick
<OK>/Next:  ⏎
<Motion description>/?:  ⏎
Command:
```

The AME command SOLCHP

This command is for changing various properties of AME primitives. When the command is called the command line shows:

Command: solchp   *key Return*
Select solid: *pick*
Color/Delete/Evaluate/Instance/Move/Next/Replace/Size/
                                               eXit/<N>:

From the options shown, it can be seen that with **SOLCHP:**

1. The colour or size of any primitive in a 3D AME solid can be changed;

2. Any primitive making up a 3D AME solid can be replaced or moved;

3. Any primitive from a 3D AME solid can be deleted;

4. A copy of any primitive in a 3D AME solid can be copied with the **i** (Instance) option. The copy will not be seen as it will be exactly on top of the primitive from which it was Instanced. However the copy can be moved and then used to replace another primitive in the solid.

Examples of the **r** (Replace), **s** (Size) and **m** (Move) options of **SOLCHP** are shown in Fig. 6.6. Note that although the given 3D AME solid is composed of three primitives, the **SOLUNION** is retained after primitives in the solid have been amended by **SOLCHP**.

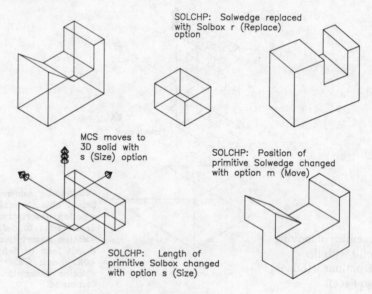

SOLCHP: Solwedge replaced with Solbox r (Replace) option

MCS moves to 3D solid with s (Size) option

SOLCHP: Position of primitive Solwedge changed with option m (Move)

SOLCHP: Length of primitive Solbox changed with option s (Size)

Fig. 6.6 Changing the properties of primitives with the **SOLCHP** options **r** (Replace, **s** (Size) and **m** (Move)

The AME command SOLSEP

SOLSEP reverses the operation of **SOLUNION**. The AME solid is separated into its constituent primitives. An example is given in Fig. 6.7. This illustration also shows the effect of the AME command **SOLMESH**. **SOLMESH** changes the wireframe into a series of Pfaces behind which hidden lines can be removed with the **HIDE** command.

The AME command SOLPURGE

When parts of an AME solid have been erased, it is advisable to call **SOLPURGE**. **SOLPURGE** can be used:

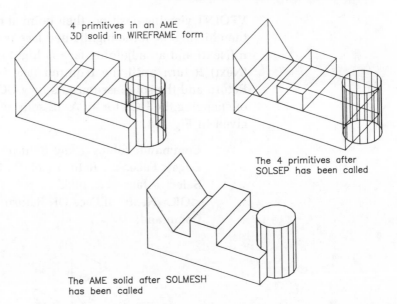

4 primitives in an AME
3D solid in WIREFRAME form

The 4 primitives after
SOLSEP has been called

Fig. 6.7 An AME solid after
the actions of **SOLSEP** and
SOLMESH

The AME solid after SOLMESH
has been called

1. To clean from memory **a** (**All**) AME primitives or AME solids which have been erased previously;
2. To reduce the size of the drawing file by calling the **m** (**Memory**), **b** (**Bfile**) and **p** (**Pmesh**) options of **SOLPURGE** in turn. The size of a drawing file acted upon in this manner can be reduced by as much as 40% or more. If these options are used, when the drawing is called from its file back to the drawing editor, the solid will have to be updated by AME. This operation automatically occurs when the first AME command is used to work on the solid. However, if the drawing is to be plotted with hidden lines removed, the file must be called back to the drawing editor and the required solid acted upon by **SOLMESH**. Otherwise, hidden lines will not be removed in the plot.

The AME command SOLUCS

By calling the command **SOLUCS** a new UCS plane, on to which details may be added, can be obtained very speedily. When the command has been called, all that is required is to select either an edge or a face of the AME solid. When the selection has been made, the model automatically aligns on a new UCS on the selected edge or face. Because one normally requires a face to be aligned as a new UCS, <**Face**> is the default option. It is easier to select a face when the AME solid is in a pictorial view. Thus, first place the solid in a

VPOINT viewing position, then point at the required face. That face then highlights. If the highlighted face is not the required one, enter **n** (Next) and an adjoining face is highlighted. Continue entering **n** (Next) *Return* until the required face is highlighted. Then press *Return* and the solid assumes its new UCS position. Two examples of changing the UCS for an AME solid with the aid of **SOLUCS** are given in Fig. 6.8.

Command: solucs   *key Return*
Edge/<Face>:   *Return* (selects the option **Face**)
Select a face ... *pick*
<OK>/Next: if Face OK *Return*, if not n (Next) *key Return*
Command:

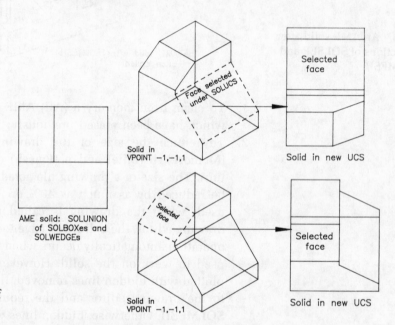

Fig. 6.8 Changing the UCS of an AME solid with **SOLUCS**

Solid in VPOINT −1,−1,1

Solid in new UCS

Face selected under SOLUCS

Selected face

AME solid: SOLUNION of SOLBOXes and SOLWEDGEs

Selected face

Solid in VPOINT −1,−1,1

Solid in new UCS

Selected face

The AME command SOLFEAT

SOLFEAT allows edges or faces (features) to be copied from an AME solid for use in other constructions or in other parts of the current drawing. After calling the command, select the required edge or face. The selected part highlights. Next call **MOVE** and move the selected edge or face from the solid to wherever it is required. Note that when an edge or a face has been acted upon by **SOLFEAT**, the solid itself is not changed. Figure 6.9 shows all the faces from an AME solid moved away from the solid. The solid itself is unchanged.

Command: solfeat   *key Return*
Edge/<Face>:   Return (selects the option **Face**)
Select a face ...   *pick*
<OK>/Next: if Face OK *Return*, if not n (Next) *key Return*
Command:

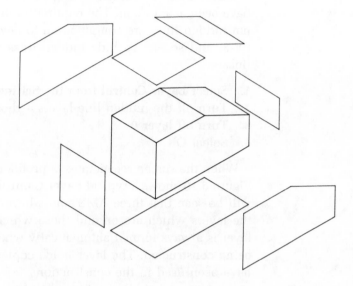

Fig. 6.9 All faces moved
from an AME solid with
SOLFEAT, yet the solid
remains unchanged

**The selected face highlights. If the highlighted face is not the
required face answer** n (Next) to the **<OK>/Next:** prompt and
another face highlights. Continue with n (Next) *Return* until the
required face is highlighted, then press *Return*. The selected edge
or face remains highlighted. Call **MOVE** to move the highlighted
edge or face away from the AME solid.

The AME command SOLPROF

SOLPROF is for removing hidden lines from AME solids. When
SOLPROF is called, the command line, its prompts, options and
possible responses show:

Command: solprof   *key Return*
Select objects: *pick* **1 selected, 1 found.**
Select objects: *Return*
Display hidden profile lines on separate layer?<N>:   y
                                                    (Yes) *Return*

1 solid selected
Profile line computation of current solid has started.

**Profile line computation of current solid is completed.
Command:**

The hidden lines are computed on to new layers automatically
formed when **SOLPROF** is in action. These layers are named 0-PH-
2, 0-PH-3, and so on, depending upon the number of solids which
have been acted upon. The required profile lines – those which are
not hidden lines are computed on to new layers named 0-PV-2, 0-
PV-3, and so on. To hide hidden lines and to show only profile
lines:

1. Select **Layer Control** from the **Settings** pull-down menu;
2. Turn off the hidden line layers – those named 0-PH;
3. Turn off layer 0;
4. Select **OK**.

When the screen regenerates, a profile only drawing will appear.
Figure 6.10 shows a typical **Layer Control** dialogue box in which it
will be seen that three AME solids have been **SOLPROF**iled. Note
the layers which are **on** and those which are **off**. The **AME_FRZ**
layer is always formed automatically when an AME solid model is
being constructed. The layer holds copies of the primitives which
have been used in the constructions.

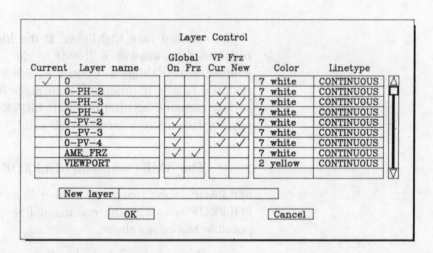

Fig. 6.10 The **Layer Control**
dialogue box showing the
layers formed when
SOLPROF is in action

Figure 6.11 is a three-viewport drawing of an AME solid before
SOLPROF is called. Figure 6.12 is the same drawing after each
viewport drawing has been acted upon by **SOLPROF**.

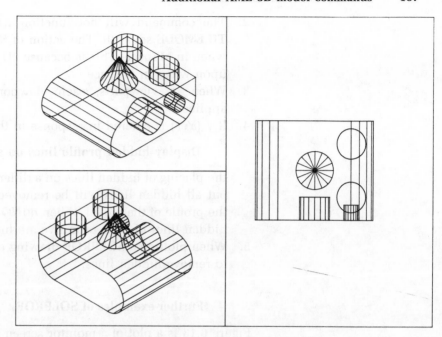

Fig. 6.11 An AME model in a three-viewport drawing editor display

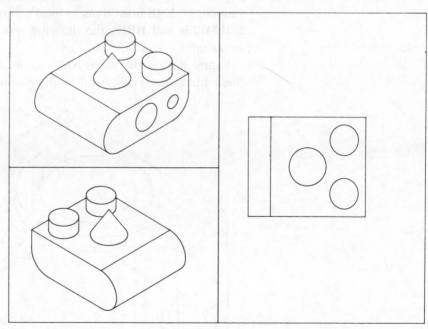

Fig. 6.12 The same AME model after **SOLPROF**

Notes on the action of SOLPROF

1. When an AME model has been acted upon by **SOLPROF**, only the current view profile is correct. If the viewing position is changed, it will be seen that the profile is no longer correct.

2. The command will not function while in **PS**pace (i.e. with **TILEMODE** set at 0). The action of **SOLPROF** is only effective when in **MS**pace. This is because 3D models can only be acted upon when in **MS**pace.

3. When in viewports, each viewport must have **SOLPROF** applied.

4. If *y* (*Yes*) is entered in response to the option

Display hidden profile lines on separate layer?<N>:

the placing of hidden lines on a different layer will take longer, but all hidden lines will be removed, including those behind the profile of the model. When *n* (*NO*) is the response, only the hidden lines of each primitive are hidden.

5. When plotting a **SOLPROF** drawing do not set the plotting run to remove hidden lines.

Further examples of SOLPROF

Figure 6.13 is a plot of a monitor screen stand, constructed from a number of AME primitives to form a single AME solid model. After **SOLMESH** and **HIDE**, the drawing was plotted with hidden lines removed.

Figure 6.14 is the same AME model as in Fig. 6.13. It has been placed in a four-viewport drawing editor layout and the drawing in

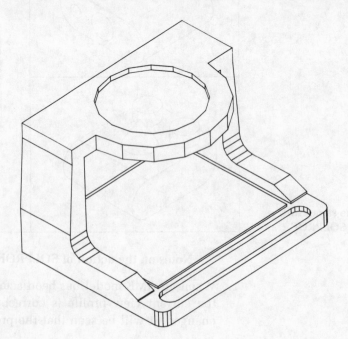

Fig. 6.13 A pictorial view of the lower half of a VDU monitor stand drawn in AME solids

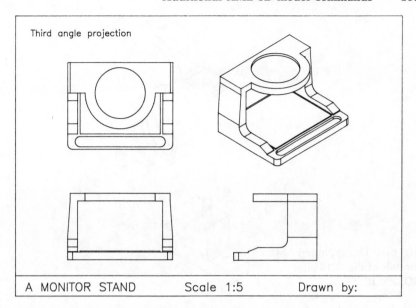

Fig. 6.14 A third angle orthographic projection of the stand (Fig. 6.13) drawn in **Viewports** after **SOLPROF**

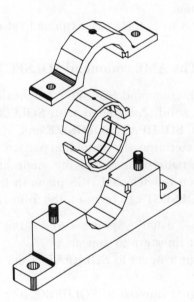

Fig. 6.15 An exploded set of AME solid models

each viewport has been profiled with the aid of **SOLPROF**. The response to the option:

Display hidden profile lines on separate layer?<N>:

was *Return (No)*, resulting in lines behind the profile itself being hidden.

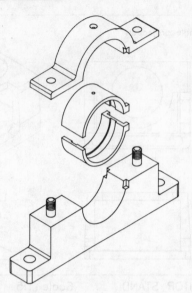

Fig. 6.16 The exploded AME models of Fig. 6.15 after **SOLPROF**

Figure 6.15 is an exploded view of a bearing, each part being an AME model.

Figure 6.16 is the same exploded set of models after **SOLPROF**.

The AME command SOLSECT

The AME command **SOLSECT** hatches defined UCS planes across an AME solid. Associated with **SOLSECT** are the three **SOLVAR** variables, **SOLHPAT**, **SOLHSIZE** and **SOLHANGLE**, the settings of which determine the hatching pattern, the spacing between the hatching pattern lines and the angle at which the hatch pattern appears on the selected UCS plane in the model. This means that before **SOLSECT** can be used, the following settings must be made:

1. UCS – usually 3point – to set the UCS plane on which the hatch lines are to appear;
2. Assign a name to **SOLHPAT** to set the hatching pattern to be used;
3. Assign a number to **SOLHSIZE** to set the hatching spacings;
4. Assign a number to **SOLHANGLE** to set the angle at which the hatching will occur.

Then all that is required is to call **SOLSECT** and *pick* the model in which the UCS section plane has been set.

An example of the use of **SOLSECT** is given in Fig. 6.17. A detailed description of the procedure for producing the complete drawing is given below.

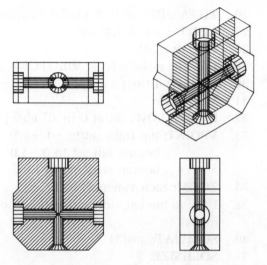

Fig. 6.17 An example of the use of **SOLSECT**

The procedure for constructing Fig. 6.17

1. Load AME
2. **UCS:** 3point: 0,0,0; 1,0,0; 0,0,1
3. **ZOOM:** 1
4. **UCS:** Save as FRONT
5. **PLINE:** as Fig. 6.18
6. **SOLEXT:** extrude-60
7. **UCS:** w (World)
8. **ZOOM:** A (All)
9. **SOLMOVE:** place model central to screen
10. **SOLCYL:** Radius 10 Height 180
11. **SOLCYL:** Radius 20 Height 20
12. **SOLCONE:** Radius 20 Height 20
13. **UCS:** Restore FRONT
14. **SOLMOVE:** the 20 Radius SOLCYL to top of model
15. **UCS:** 3point to obtain an end view
16. **UCS:** Save as ENDVIEW
17. **ZOOM:** a (All)
18. **SOLCYL:** Radius 10 Height 180
19. **SOLCYL:** Radius 20 Height 20
20. **UCS:** Restore FRONT
21. **SOLMOVE:** SOLCYLs to required positions
22. **COPY:** Copy SOLCYL of height 20 to top of model
23. **UCS:** w (WORLD)
24. **ZOOM:** a (All)
25. **SOLUNION:** all SOLCYLs and the SOLCONE

26. **TILEMODE:** set to 0 Model disappears. In Paper Space
27. **LIMITS:** set to 420,300
28. **ZOOM:** a (All)
29. **LAYER:** make a layer VIEWPORT, colour 2 (Yellow)
30. **MVIEW:** 4 (four viewport screen) and f (Fit)
31. **MSPACE:**
32. **UCSFOLLOW:** set at 0 in all viewports except top left
33. **VPOINT:** top right set to −1,−1,1;
    bottom left set to 0,−1,0;
    bottom right set to 1,0,0
34. **ZOOM:** each viewport to 1
35. **UCS:** in top left viewport only – 3point along vertical centre of model
36. **SOLHPAT:** ansi31
37. **SOLHSIZE:** 3
38. **SOLHANGLE:** −90
39. **SOLSECT:** in top left viewport only *pick* the model

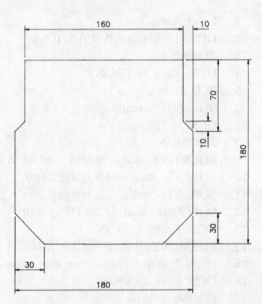

Fig. 6.18 The pline outline
for the example Fig. 6.17

Another example of a model with a **SOLSECT** section is given on Fig. 6.19. The left-hand of the pair of drawings in Fig. 6.19 is before the sectioned half model was acted upon with **SOLPROF**. The right-hand drawing is of the model after the action of **SOLPROF**.

Removing the section plane from a SOLSECT

The surface outline and the hatching of a **SOLSECT** section consists

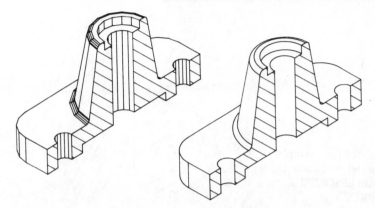

Fig. 6.19 Another 3D model
showing the use of
SOLSECT

of two blocks – the outline and the hatching. These can be moved
from the model and used as two-dimensional sectional views.
Some additional lines will usually have to be added to complete
such a sectional view. **SOLSECT** sectional views obtained in this
manner are correct, in that they have been derived from models
which can be viewed from a variety of directions to check their
accuracy. Figure 6.20 shows the **SOLSECT** plane and its hatching
moved from the half model of Fig. 6.19, together with a completed
and dimensioned orthographic 2D view. Another example of an
AME model acted upon by **SOLSECT** is shown in Fig. 6.21. This
example has also been profiled with the aid of **SOLPROF**.

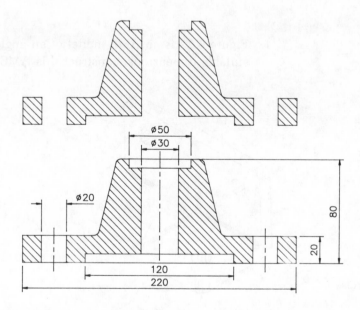

Fig. 6.20 The section plane
of Fig. 6.19 used as a
sectional view

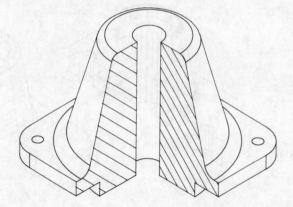

Fig. 6.21 A further example
of a 3D model constructed
with the aid of **SOLSECT**
and **SOLPROF**

The AME SOLVAR variables

In the same way in which variables can be set in AutoCAD, so can
variables be set in the AME extension. A list of the AME **SOLVAR**
variables will appear on a flipped text screen if the command
SOLVAR is called and a ? entered as the choice of option.

Exercises

The following exercises are included here to allow the reader to
practise the use of AME in the construction of 3D model drawings.
The exercises contain elements of the commands included in this
and the last chapter.

1. Figure 6.22 is an AME model of an angle support. Working to
    suitable dimensions, construct this AME model.

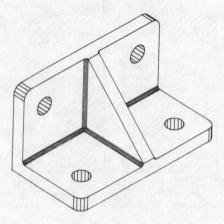

Fig. 6.22 Exercise 1

2. Figure 6.23 is an AME model of a supporting device. Working
    to suitable dimensions construct the model.

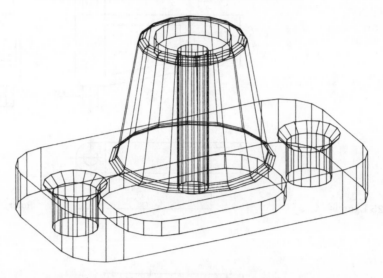

Fig. 6.23 Exercise 2

3. Figure 6.24 is a three-view orthographic projection of a simple
    Sellotape dispenser. Construct an AME model of the dispenser
    to the given dimensions.

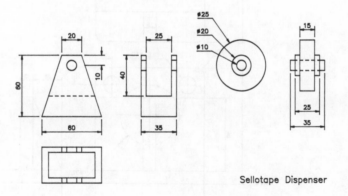

Fig. 6.24 Exercise 3

Sellotape Dispenser

4. Figure 6.25 is a three-view orthographic projection of a rotary
    bracket. Construct an AME solid drawing to the dimensions
    given.
5. Figure 6.26 is a three-view orthographic projection of a support
    clip. Construct an AME model drawing of the clip to the
    dimensions given.
6. Figure 6.27 is a three-view orthographic projection of an
    electronic hand control device. Construct an AME model
    drawing of the device to the dimensions given.

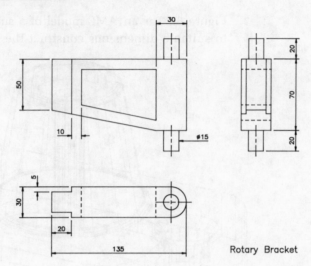

Fig. 6.25 Exercise 4

Rotary Bracket

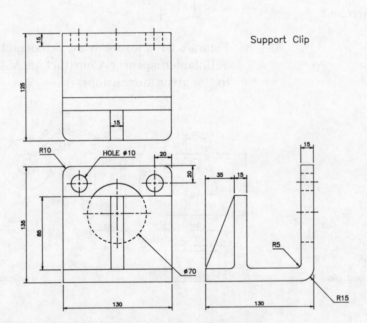

Support Clip

Fig. 6.26 Exercise 5

7. Figure 6.28 is a three-view orthographic projection of a hanging bracket. Construct an AME model drawing of the bracket to the dimensions given.

8. Figure 6.29 is a **VPOINT** view of a table constructed with the aid of AME. Using dimensions of your own choice, construct a similar 3D model.

Electronic Hand Control
Device

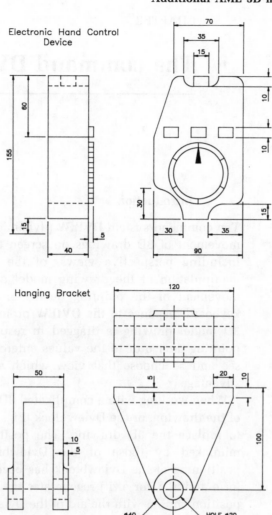

Fig. 6.27 Exercise 6

Hanging Bracket

Fig. 6.28 Exercise 7

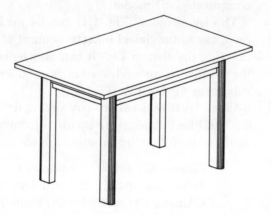

Fig. 6.29 Exercise 8

CHAPTER 7

The command DVIEW

Introduction

The command system **DVIEW** (dynamic view) allows the dynamic movement of 3D drawings on screen to produce pictorial views, including perspective views, of the model being drawn. The manipulation of the drawing model can be controlled either by movement of the pointing device or by entering values at the keyboard response to the **DVIEW** prompts. A ghosted copy of the 3D model drawing is dragged in response to movements of the pointing device or to the values entered, allowing the operator to see and so choose that view which shows the drawing to best advantage.

When working with a complicated 3D drawing, either only a part of the drawing, or the Dviewblock (Fig. 7.1) can be called to screen to replace the 3D drawing. The positions of the 3D model are mimicked by those of the Dviewblock. When the required positioning of the Dviewblock has been selected, pressing Return (or entering X for eXit) regenerates the original 3D drawing in the position chosen with the aid of the Dviewblock. The value of using the Dviewblock is that, being a 3D line drawing, it will regenerate much more quickly as it is moved to new positions, than would a complicated 3D model.

The Dviewblock (Fig. 7.1) can be made to appear on screen in response to the **Select objects:** prompt of the **DVIEW** command by pressing the Return key. It can also be selected at any time while the **DVIEW** command system is in operation from the on-screen sub-menu for **DVIEW** (Fig. 7.2).

When **DVIEW** is called – by keying **dv** (**dv**iew), by selection from the **DISPLAY** on-screen menu, or from the **Display** pull-down menu – the following prompts appear at the command line:

> **Command:** dview   *key Return*
> **Select objects:** either by *picking* or in a window *Return*
> **CAmera/TArget/Distance/POints/PAn/Zoom/TWist/CLip/**
>   **Hide/Off/Undo/<eXit>:**

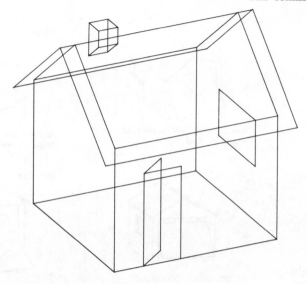

Fig. 7.1 The AutoCAD
Dviewblock

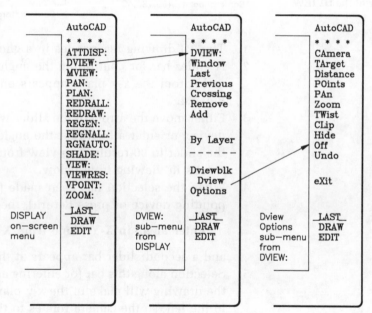

Fig. 7.2 The **DISPLAY** on-
screen menu and the **DVIEW**
sub-menus

The CAmera option

Key ca (**CA**mera), or select **CA**mera from a menu; the prompt
changes to:

Enter angle from X-Y plane <23>:

and the screen changes – see Fig. 7.4:

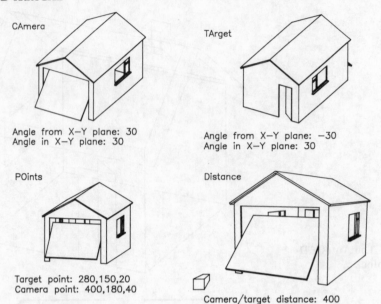

CAmera

Angle from X—Y plane: 30
Angle in X—Y plane: 30

TArget

Angle from X—Y plane: −30
Angle in X—Y plane: 30

POints

Target point: 280,150,20
Camera point: 400,180,40

Distance

Camera/target distance: 400

Fig. 7.3 Drawings resulting
from four of the **DVIEW**
options

1. The 3D drawing regenerates in a ghosted form.
2. A slider bar for controlling the angle which the drawing is to make from the x-y plane appears on the right of the screen – Fig. 7.4.
3. Either move the arrow of the slider with the aid of the pointing device, or enter a figure for the angle at the keyboard. Moving the slider to 90 results in a view from above. Moving it to −90 results in viewing from below.
4. When the selection has been made (press the *pick* key of the pointing device or press *Return*), the prompt changes to.

Enter angle in X-Y plane from X axis <−90>:

and a second slider bar appears at the top of the screen.
5. Selection along this bar (or entering an angle) controls the angle the drawing will make in the x-y plane. As the slider is moved to the left, so the camera rotates to the left. Move the slider to the right and the camera rotates right.
6. As the selections on either of the two slider bars are made, the ghosted drawing is dragged to new positions.
7. Finally, pressing the *pick* key or *Return* regenerates the original 3D drawing in the selected view (see Fig. 7.3).
8. As either slider bar is moved, so figures for the angle are updated continuously at the status line.

The figures in brackets (<>) after each prompt show the default angles from and in the x-y plane of the last position of the 3D

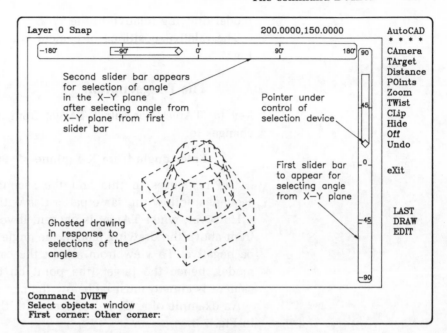

Fig. 7.4 The screen when the option **CA**mera is called

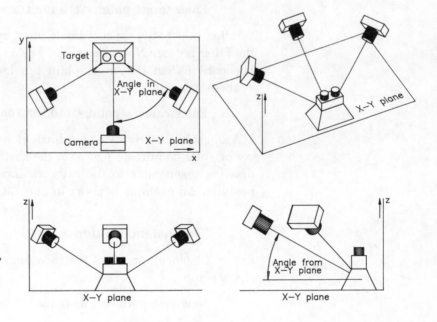

Fig. 7.5 Plan, view from rear, side view and pictorial view of imaginary camera and target positions

model drawing relative to the WCS.

The relative positions of camera and drawing are described in Fig. 7.5.

The TArget option

Key ta (TArget), or select TArget from a menu, and the prompt changes to:

Enter angle from X-Y plane <−90>:

The responses to this and the second prompt of the TArget sequence, follow the same pattern as with the CAmera prompt.

However, when TArget is chosen, if you wish to choose a view from above the drawing model, the angle from the x-y plane must be negative. To view from above, the camera must be above the model, hence the target (the point on the model at which the camera is aimed) must be below the camera.

An example of a view produced with the TArget option is given in Fig. 7.3.

The POints option

Key po (POints), or select POints from a menu, and the prompts appear:

Enter target point <210,152,152>:

Either select an x,y,z coordinate point by pointing with the aid of the Filter .xy (see Notes below), or Key an x,y,z coordinate from the keyboard. When the target point has been selected, the prompt changes to:

Enter camera point <210,152,200)>:

Again select a new x,y,z coordinate point with the aid of the filter .xy or enter coordinate figures at the keyboard. The ghosted screen drawing regenerates to the original drawing in its new selected position. An example is given in Fig. 7.3.

The Distance option

Key d (Distance), or select Distance from a menu, and the prompt changes to:

New camera/target distance <150>:

and a slider bar appears at the top of the screen. Points on the slider are numbered from 0× to 16× (0 times to 16 times). Moving the slider arrow under the control of the pointing device changes the distance between the target drawing and the camera and either increases or decreases the size of the drawing. Its size can also be controlled by entering a figure at the keyboard. If the drawing appears so large that only a small part of it is showing on screen, key a large number, e.g. 400. This will decrease the size considerably allowing further distance changes to be made. Note that drawings produced with the aid of the **D**istance prompt are perspective views. A perspective icon appears bottom left of the screen – but only if the UCS icon is set **ON**.

An example of a perspective drawing is included in Fig. 7.6. A second example of a more complicated 3D model drawing is given in Fig. 7.7.

The Zoom option

Key z (**Z**oom), or select **Z**oom from a menu, and the prompt changes to:

Adjust lens length <11.5>:

and a slider bar appears at the top of the screen similar to the **D**istance slider bar. Either move the pointer of the slider bar to a desired position, watching the ghosted drawing changing size as the movement takes place; Or enter a figure at the keyboard, noting

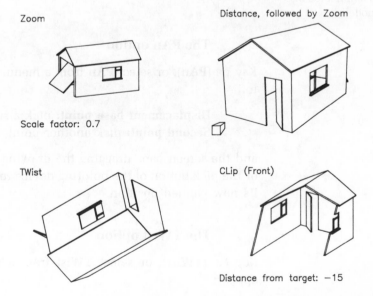

Fig. 7.6 Drawings resulting from four further **DVIEW** options

that as the pointing device is moved so the lens length is updated at the upper right corner of the screen. (See Fig. 7.6.)

Using **Zoom** in **DVIEW** alters the size of the drawing model, as does **Distance**. However the **Distance** option is for perspective views and the **Zoom** option is for views in parallel projection. If the drawing is in perspective, as a result of employing the **Distance** option and the option **Zoom** is then called, the lens length of the camera is constantly up-dated at the status line as the pointing device adjusts the slider bar. If the drawing is in parallel projection when the option **Zoom** is called, a scale factor figure is constantly updated on the status line. Figures for the scale factor (in parallel views) or the lens length (for perspective views) can also be entered at the keyboard.

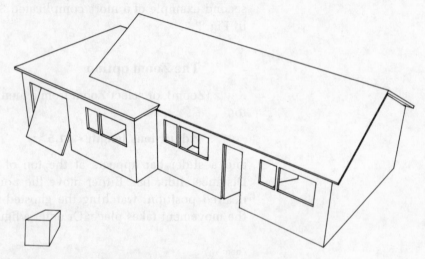

Fig. 7.7 A perspective view of a more complicated 3D drawing model

The PAn option

Key pa (**PAn**), or select **PAn** from a menu, and the prompts change to:

> **Displacement base point:** *pick* a suitable point *Return*
> **Second point:** *pick* another point

and the screen pans dragging the drawing with it. Pressing *Return* or the *pick* button of the pointing device regenerates the drawing in its new panned position.

The TWist option

Key tw (**TWist**), or select **TWist** from a menu, and the prompts appear:

New view twist <0,00>:

and a rubber band line appears on screen attached between the 3D model drawing (or Dviewblock) and the cross-cursors hairs. Moving the cursor cross-hairs under the control of the pointing device rotates (twists) the ghosted model drawing to new positions in a rotary manner. When satisfied with a position, pressing the *pick* button regenerates the original drawing in its new position.

The CLip option

Key cl (**CL**ip), or select **CL**ip from a menu, and the prompts appear:

Back/Front/>Off>:

Either the back or the front of the drawing can be clipped by *keying* a b or an f. Figure 7.6 shows a 3D drawing which has been clipped at the front at a distance of −15 from the camera.

If a front clip is required, *key* f and the command line prompt changes to:

Eye/<Distance from target> <430>:

together with a slider bar at the top of the screen. Moving the pointer on the bar, or *keying* a figure, watch the ghosted drawing to determine when the clipping is at the required position on your drawing. The drawing regenerates as clipped, when *Return* or the *pick* button of the pointing device is pressed.

Entering e (**Eye**), when in perspective view places the clipping plane at the camera. Any objects then behind the camera do not appear on screen. Eye also causes a previously placed front clipping plane to revert to its camera position.

The Hide option

Key h (**Hide**), or select **Hide** from a menu, and the prompts appear:

Removing hidden lines: 175

and hidden lines are automatically removed.

This has the same effect while in the **DVIEW** command as the command **HIDE** has when DVIEW is not in operation.

The Off option

Keying o (**Off**) turns perspective views off and thus into parallel views. When **Distance** is invoked, perspective views are turned on again.

The Undo option

Keying u (Undo) reverses (undoes) the last **DVIEW** operation, without coming out of the **DVIEW** system.

The eXit option

Key X (eXit) and the **DVIEW** command is cancelled, leaving the drawing on screen as amended by **DVIEW**. Pressing the *Return* key or the *pick* key of the pointing device has the same effect.

General notes about the DVIEW command

1. Any details entered while in **DVIEW** – e.g. points – are relative to the World Coordinate System (WCS) and not to the current UCS (unless it is the UCS World).
2. When **DVIEW** is called, the pull-down menus are not available.
3. If a filter (e.g. .xy) is required, either *Key .xy*, or select *.xy* from either the **Line** or **3Dface** on-screen menus.
4. Flipping the screen between drawing editor and information screen by pressing F1, is not possible when in **DVIEW**.
5. After each prompt option is completed, the command line reverts to:

   CAmera/TArget/Distance/POints/PAn/Zoom/TWist/CLip/
   Hide/Off/Undo/<eXit>:

   ready for the next option. To get out of the **DVIEW** command system, press *Return* or enter x (eXit).
6. **Zoom** or **Pan** cannot be used, when in perspective view (after using **Distance**) after coming out of **DVIEW**. If either command is attempted, a message:

   *** This command may not be invoked in a perspective view ***

   appears at the command line;
7. Similarly, when in a perspective view, it is not possible to use **DRAW** commands by pointing, although they can be used by entering coordinates at the keyboard.

CHAPTER 8

AutoShade

Introduction

The AutoCAD command SHADE

Before dealing with the stand-alone package AutoShade, try the command **SHADE** in AutoCAD. An example of using this command is given in Plate 6. This plate shows the action of **SHADE** on the AME model, fig. 7.7 (page 124). All that is required is to call the command and the model is shaded according to the colours in which each part was constructed. The type of shading resulting from the command is controlled by entering one of the figures 0 to 3 in response to the Set variable **SHADEDGE**:

1. **SHADEDGE** set at 0: Faces are shaded but edges not high-lighted – but only with a 256-colour display.

2. **SHADEDGE** set at 1: Faces are shaded, edges highlighted in background colour – but only with a 256-colour display.

3. **SHADEDGE** set at 2: Edges are shaded on the colour in which the faces were drawn. Faces are black. Hidden edges are hidden.

4. **SHADEDGE** set at 3: Faces are shaded in the colour in which they were drawn.

Plate 6 shows the results of calling **SHADE** with **SHADEDGE** set at 3.

AutoShade

AutoShade is a stand-alone, post-processing software package for rendering 3D models constructed in AutoCAD. The results of shading with the software are illustrated in Plates 4, 5 and 7. The renderings for these plates were prepared with Version 2 of AutoShade. Version 2 can be obtained either with or without another rendering program, Renderman. Although the AutoShade plates in this book show the use of Version 2 with Renderman, no renderings made with Renderman are included here. With Renderman, excellent renderings can be achieved in a number of colours, in different materials and with a variety of backgrounds.

Note on display hardware

The models shown in colour plates in this book were all rendered on a VGA colour screen with the appropriate colour card. Close observation of the colour plates will show that edges are not clean, showing up in somewhat jagged lines (**jaggies**). This is because when working with AutoShade a VGA screen renders at 320×280 resolution.

filmrolls

To render a 3D model in AutoShade a filmroll file (extension *.flm*) must first be prepared in AutoCAD. In this chapter, short descriptions of the rendering in AutoShade of three of the 3D models seen in earlier chapters will be given, together with a fourth example – an AME model for which a description of constructing the model in AutoCAD is given.

When in the AutoShade editor, all operations are performed with the aid of the pointing device (usually a mouse) and a series of pull-down menus, dialogue boxes and message boxes. The settings for lights and camera saved with the filmroll can be amended if thought necessary once the filmroll has been loaded into Auto-Shade.

Preparing a filmroll

The procedure for preparing and saving a filmroll file is:

1. Construct the required 3D model in AutoCAD.
2. Call UCS ***WORLD*** so that the model is in plan view.
3. If necessary scale the model to a suitable size.
4. Move the model to a suitable position.
5. Call the command **ASHADE**, which loads the file *ashade.lsp*. The commands in **ASHADE** then appear in the on-screen menu area (fig. 8.1).

6. Add lights to the drawing – at least one pointed light – usually above the model – and at least one directed light, but two (or more) usually give better illumination to the model in its scene (see fig. 8.1).
7. Add a camera.
8. Check that the camera gives a good view of the model by calling **CAMVIEW**. If not, erase the camera and install another with different target and camera position points.
9. Call the command **SCENE** and select the lights and camera for the scene.
10. Call the command **fiLMROLL** and save the filmroll after entering a suitable filename for the filmroll in the dialogue box.

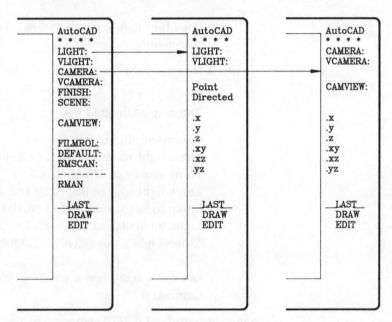

Fig. 8.1 The AutoCAD on-screen **ASHADE** and **RMAN** menus

Adding lights to an AutoShade scene

Select **LIGHT:** from the **ASHADE** menu and the **Lights** sub-menu appears as in fig. 8.1. Lights can be positioned at any coordinate point with the aid of filters from the sub-menu, or by entering the x,y,z coordinate numbers as in the following examples. first a name for the light is required – any suitable name (e.g. LIGHT01). Then when a **P**oint light is requested (response **P**), only its height (z coordinate) above a point on the WCS is required (x,y coordinates). If, however a **D**irected light is required – one directed at a targeted point on the model being lit – then both the light target point and the position of the light itself are required. When light positions have been selected, an icon appears on screen, its shape depending whether the light is a **Point or a D**irected light. These icons are included in fig. 8.3.

Entering a Point light

Command: light *key Return*
Enter light name: LIGHT01   *key Return*
Point source or Directed <P>: *Return*
Enter light location: 300,200,200 *key Return*
Light intensity <1.0>: *Return*
Name/Light color (RGB) <1.000000,1.000000,1.000000>:

Return

Does this light cast a shadow? Yes<No>:   *Return*
Command:

and an icon for LIGHT01 appears at the required location.

Entering a Directed light

Command: light   *key Return*
Enter light name: LIGHT02 *key Return*
Point source or Directed <P>: d **(D**irected)   *key Return*
Enter light aim point: 250,180,40 *key Return*
Enter light location: 130,20,100 *key Return*
Light intensity <1.0>: 0.5 *key Return*
Name/Light color (RGB) <1.000000,1.000000,1.000000>:

Return

Does this light cast a shadow? Yes<No>: *Return*
Command:

and an icon for LIGHT02 appears at the required location.
If more than one **D**irected light is required, the command and prompt sequences would be, for example, as follows:

Command: light   *key Return*
Enter light name: LIGHT03 *key Return*
Point source or Directed <P>: d **(D**irected) *key Return*
Enter light aim point: 250,180,30 *key Return*
Enter light location: 130,20,200 *key Return*
Light intensity <1.0>: *Return*
Name/Light color (RGB) <1.000000,1.000000,1.000000>:

Return

Does this light cast a shadow? Yes<No>: *Return*
Command:

and a drawing of LIGHT03 appears at the required location.

Adding cameras to an AutoShade scene

In AutoShade the 3D model being rendered will appear as if seen from a camera lens. The target point of the camera and its position are set as in the following example:

Command: camera   *key Return*
Enter camera name: CAMERA01 *key Return*
Enter target point: 270,180,30   *key Return*
Enter camera location: 170,10,90 *key Return*
Command:

and the icon for a CAMERA01 appears at the designated point. Note the camera icon shows the direction at which it is pointing.

The ASHADE command CAMVIEW

At this stage, it is advisable to check whether the camera and its target point are at suitable coordinate positions. This is easily achieved with the aid of the **camview** command as follows:

Command: camview   *key Return*
Select the camera: *pick* icon of CAMERA01
Command:

and a perspective view of the model appears on screen in a position as if seen by the camera. Note the perspective icon at the bottom right of the screen. Because it is a perspective view, neither a zoom nor the adding of drawing details is possible. When using **CAMVIEW**, remember to enter u (**u**ndo) after viewing the camview drawing. If not satisfied with the camera target point and position, enter a second u (Undo) to remove the camera icon. Then set a new camera with coordinates judged from the viewing errors noted in the **CAMVIEW** scene.

The ASHADE command SCENE

Having satisfied oneself of the lighting and camera positions, before a filmroll file is saved, call the command **SCENE**, then make appropriate responses to the prompts which appear.

Command: scene   *key Return*
Enter scene name: scene01   *key Return*

Select the camera: *pick icon of camera01*
Select a light: *pick icon of LIGHT01*
Select a light: *pick icon of LIGHT02*
Select a light: *pick icon of LIGHT03*
Select a light: *Return*
Enter scene location: *pick* **a suitable spot on screen**
Command:

and the scene icon – a clapper board with the camera and light names – appears at the *picked* spot.

More than one camera can be set in for a filmroll layout, but only one camera can be saved with any one scene. Thus several cameras in a variety of positions would be set at as many scenes as there are cameras.

Saving a filmroll file

Finally, when lights and camera positions have been set and the scene identified with its icon on screen, call the command **filMROLL** and save to a file with an appropriate name.

Command: filmroll *key Return*

enter name in **Create filmroll file** dialogue box

Creating the filmroll file:
Processing face: a series of numbers appears on the prompt
line
Command:

and the filmroll file is saved to the entered name. Note its file extension will be *.flm*.

Examples of scenes for filmrolls

Example 1 – a pair of poppet valves

See Fig. 3.18 (page 62), repeated here as Fig. 8.2. The filmroll scene for this pair of models is given in Fig. 8.3. In this scene, three lights have been included – a **P**oint light above the two models and two **D**irected lights aimed at the models. The camera is set besides the second light. This is a typical lights and camera layout for such a filmroll. The AutoShade rendering of this model is shown in Plate 4.

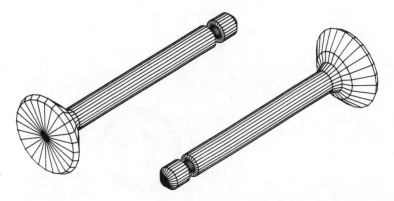

Fig. 8.2 **VPOINT** view of two poppet valves

Fig. 8.3 Lights, camera and scene settings for a filmroll of the two valves from Fig. 8.2

Example 2 – a bevel gear

See Fig. 2.41 (page 47) – a model constructed from Rulesurf surfaces. The filmroll scene for this model is shown in Fig. 8.4, together with their coordinate positions. Again, three lights – a **P**oint and two **D**irection lights. Note that LIGHT02 illuminates the model from behind and below. A **CAMVIEW** of the model is given in Fig. 8.5.

(970,280,−50)

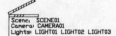

Scene: SCENE01
Camera: CAMERA01
Lights: LIGHT01 LIGHT02 LIGHT03

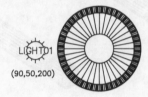

LIGHT01

(90,50,200)

(350,90,120)

(350,50,150)

Fig. 8.4 Lights, camera and scene settings for a filmroll of the bevel gear (Fig. 2.41)

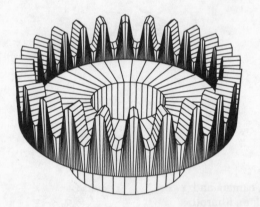

Fig. 8.5 A **CAMVIEW** view of the bevel gear from Fig. 8.4

Example 3 – a garage constructed in AME

This model was constructed in a three-viewport layout as shown in Fig. 8.6. The model was illuminated by four lights as shown in Fig. 8.7. The coordinate positions of the four lights and of the camera are included in Fig. 8.7. A **CAMVIEW** of the garage from CAMERA01 is given in Fig. 8.8.

The AutoShade rendering of this model is shown in Plate 5.

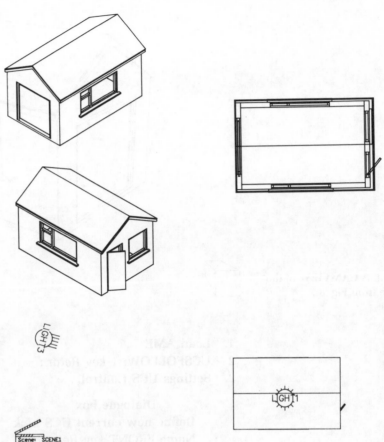

Fig. 8.6 A three-viewport scene for constructing a 3D model of a garage

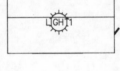

Fig. 8.7 Lights, camera and scene settings for a filmroll of the garage (Fig. 8.6)

LIGHT1 (P):	300,240,200
LIGHT2 (D):	420,50,100
LIGHT3 (D):	50,300,150
LIGHT4 (D):	80,40,120
CAMERA1:	120,40,120

Example 4 – a dressing table bottle

Creating the AME solid

The procedure for constructing the AME solid for this example is given below. Two illustrations of this example are included in this book – the first in AutoShade, the second in 3D Studio (Chapter 9).

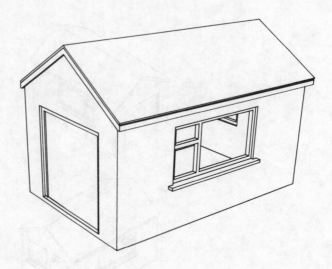

Fig. 8.8 A **CAMVIEW** of the garage from Fig. 8.7

1. **Load AME**
2. **UCSFOLLOW:** 1 *key Return*
3. **Settings UCS Control...**

    > **Dialogue box**
    > **Define new current UCS** *pick*
    > **Name** FRONT *key Return*
    > **Origin, X-axis, Plane** *pick*
    > **Origin point:** 0,0,0 *Return*
    > **Point on positive part of the X-axis:** 1,0,0 *Return*
    > **Point on positive-Y portion of the UCS X-Y plane:** 0,0,1 *key*
    > *Return*

    Command:

4. **ZOOM** 1
5. **PLINE** Draw outline of the container body on UCS **FRONT** (Fig. 8.9)
6. **SOLEXTRUDE**

    > **Select objects:** *pick the pline*
    > **Height of extrusion:** 25 *key Return*
    > **Extrusion taper angle from Z <0>:** *Return*
    > **Command:**

7. **COLOR** 2 (yellow) *key Return*
8. **PLINE** Draw a half-outline of the cap (Fig. 8.9).

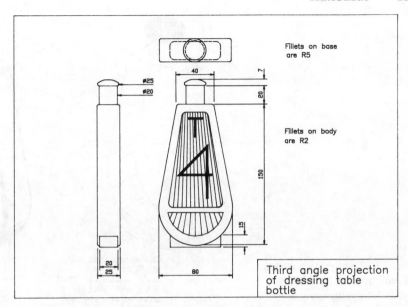

Fillets on base are R5

Fillets on body are R2

Third angle projection of dressing table bottle

Fig. 8.9 An orthographic projection with dimensions of a dressing table bottle

9. **SOLREV**

   Select objects: *pick the half-outline of the cap.*
   Axis of revolution <Start point of axis>: *pick*
   End point of axis: *pick*
   Included angle <full circle>: *Return*
   Command:

10. **UCS** w (World) *key Return*
11. **SOLMOVE** Move the cap to its central position on the body.
12. **COLOR** 7 (white)
13. **SOLBOX**

    Corner of box: *pick*
    Cube/Length/Other corner: *pick*
    Height: 15 *key Return*
    Command:

14. **UCS** r (Restore) *Key Return*

    ?/Name of UCS to restore: FRONT *key Return*
    Command:

15. **SOLMOVE** Move so that the bottom of the base is resting at y = 0.
16. **VPOINT** −1,−1,1 *key Return* (Fig. 8.10).
17. **ZOOM** window to make 3D model as large as possible.
18. **SOLFILL** front and back edges of the body to R2. Fillet base corners to R5.

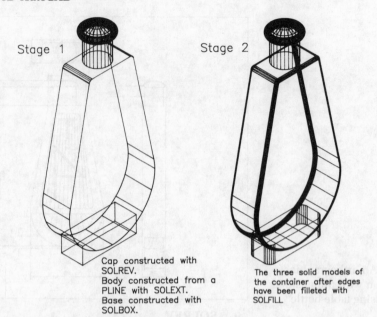

Stage 1

Stage 2

Cap constructed with
SOLREV.
Body constructed from a
PLINE with SOLEXT.
Base constructed with
SOLBOX.

The three solid models of
the container after edges
have been filleted with
SOLFILL

Fig. 8.10 The first two stages
of constructing an AME 3D
model of the dressing table
bottle

19. **SOLUNION** the base to the body.
20. **SOLMESH** body/base and cap separately.
21. **UCS** w (World) *key Return*.
22. **SOLUCS** Make the front of the model the new UCS and **S**ave
     as **LABEL**.
23. **PLINE** Draw the two parts of the label. Top part in colour 4
     (cyan) and bottom part in colour 3 (green).
24. **RULESURF** the two parts of the label
25. **COLOR** 1 (red) *key Return*
26. **TRACE**

     Trace width: 3 *key Return*
     From point: *pick*
     To point: *pick* and so on to draw the T and the 4 on the
     label
     Command:

27. **UCS** w (World) *key Return*
28. **ZOOM** a (All) *key Return*
29. **MOVE** the whole solid to a new position as in Fig. 8.11.

The filmroll scene settings showing lights and a camera for an
AutoShade rendering of this model are given in Fig. 8.12.

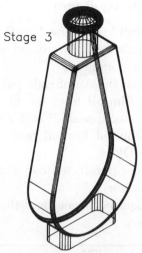

Stage 3

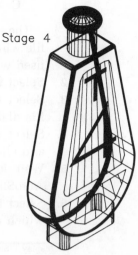

Stage 4

Fig. 8.11 The third and
fourth stages of constructing
an AME 3D model of the
dressing table bottle

The three solid models after
body and base have been
acted upon by SOLUNION

Labels added — Plines
Trace lines and Rulesurf

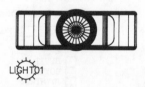

LIGHT01

Scene: SCENE01
Camera: CAMERA01
Lights: LIGHT01 LIGHT02 LIGHT03 LIGHT04

Fig. 8.12 Lights, camera and
scene settings for a filmroll
for AutoShade of the
dressing table bottle Fig. 8.9

LIGHT02
LIGHT04

CAMERA01 LIGHT03

The AutoShade editor

Once the filmroll is created, it can be loaded into AutoShade as
follows:

1. Load the AutoShade program, usually by:

C:\\> shade *key Return*

The exact call for loading AutoShade depends upon the batch file which loads the software and upon the version of MS-DOS used with the computer.

2. Select **file** from the AutoShade pull-down menu bar.

3. Select **Open filmroll** from the **file** menu. The **Select filmroll file** dialogue box appears (Fig. 8.13).

4. Select the required filmroll from the **Select filmroll file** box and click on **OK**.

5. Wait for the filmroll to load (message on prompt line of AutoShade editor).

6. Select the required Scene from the **Select Scene** dialogue box which appears.

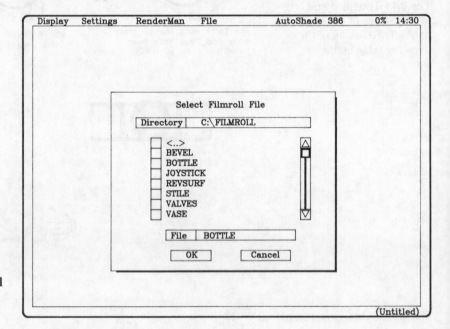

Fig. 8.13 The **Select Filmroll File** dialogue box from the AutoShade editor

Rendering the scene

Once the filmroll has been loaded:

1. Select Display from the menus along the menu bar. The Display menu (Fig. 8.14) appears;

2. Select one of the display choices as required:
   Plan View: Example Plate 2.
   Wireframe: Example Plate 3.
   Quick Shade;

Fast Shade;

Full Shade: Examples Plates 5 and 7.

3.   Wait until the selected type of rendering appears on screen.

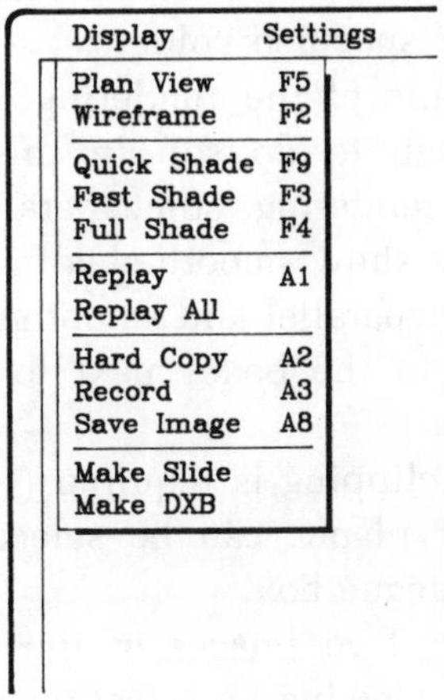

Display	Settings
Plan View	F5
Wireframe	F2
Quick Shade	F9
Fast Shade	F3
Full Shade	F4
Replay	A1
Replay All	
Hard Copy	A2
Record	A3
Save Image	A8
Make Slide	
Make DXB	

Fig. 8.14 The **Display** pull-down menu from the AutoShade editor

Modifying a rendering

This book only deals with AutoShade to a very limited extent, sufficient to illustrate to the reader some possibilities of renderings with the software. Thus the following is far from being a detailed description of the modifications which can be made to a rendering once a filmroll has been loaded and a scene selected for rendering. The reader is advised to experiment with different settings for some simple models in filmroll files. Such hands-on experimentation will give the reader a better understanding of the range of modifications which can be made when rendering scenes from filmrolls.

The pull-down menu Settings

Click on **Settings** in the **Menu** bar and the pull-down menu shown in Fig. 8.15 appears on screen. This menu lists the settings which can be amended in the rendered model of a scene from a filmroll. In this book only a couple of settings from the **Shading Model** options and **Expert** options will be included. Settings for the following elements in a rendering can be changed:

1. (a)   Camera: the angle in the X-Y plane and from the X-Y plane of the camera to the model;
    (b)   The distance of the camera from the model;
    (c)   The camera lens length.

2. Lights: The intensity of the light.
3. Surface Finishes: If surface finishes have been applied (by colours of elements in the model).
4. Create finishes: Various factors connected with surfaces can be amended for specified colours.
5. Expert: Details of the rendering can be amended (if one is expert enough to do so). In this book, some plates show perspective rendering, some parallel renderings. Most of the colour plates show smooth shading.

   Perspective/parallel and smooth/normal shading are selected by clicking in the boxes next to these items in the **Expert** dialogue box.
6. Clipping: If clipping is required (see Chapter 7), positions for the clipping planes can be selected in the **Clipping Specifications** dialogue box.
7. Stereo Pairs: Two images of the scene can be rendered for stereoscopic viewing by selection in the **Stereo Pairs Generation** dialogue box.
8. Statistics: The dialogue box which appears when Statistics is selected shows statistical details of the model from the loaded filmroll.

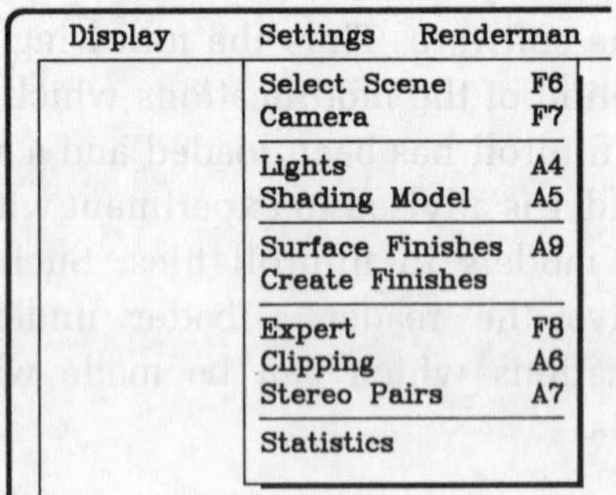

Display	Settings	Renderman
	Select Scene	F6
	Camera	F7
	Lights	A4
	Shading Model	A5
	Surface Finishes	A9
	Create Finishes	
	Expert	F8
	Clipping	A6
	Stereo Pairs	A7
	Statistics	

Fig. 8.15 The **Settings** pull-down menu from the AutoShade editor

Changing the background colour of a scene

When a scene is rendered without first modifying its background colour, the background will show black. If one wishes to change the background colour click on **Shading Model** in the **Settings** pull-down menu and the **Shading Model** dialogue box appears. To amend the background colour of a scene, click on **0 Black** in the box next to **Background** colour in the dialogue box. A second dialogue box appears over the **Shading Model** box. Click on the box opposite a named colour and the background colour for the rendering will be that selected colour. An example of a background colour selected in this manner is seen in Plate 7.

Two Expert Specifications modifications

The default projection for a scene rendered in AutoShade is perspective. To change to parallel projection, click on **Settings** in the menu bar, click on **Expert** in the menu that appears and click in the box next to the word **Perspective** in the **Expert Specifications** dialogue box. finally, click on **OK** in this box. The scene will then render in parallel projection.

To change to smooth shading click on **Smooth Shading** in the **Expert Specifications** dialogue box and the scene will be rendered with smooth shading.

Saving settings

If the scene is rendered as desired after settings have been changed, the selected settings can be saved in a script file as follows:

1. Click on **file** in the menu bar.
2. Click on **Save Settings**. The **Save Settings** dialogue box appears.
3. Enter the required directory and file name in the **file Name** box.
4. Click on **OK** and the file is saved in the named directory with a file extension *.scr*.

To call a script file, click on **file** in the **Menu** bar, click on the filename in the **Select Script file** dialogue box which appears, then click on **OK**. The filmroll, the selected scene and the settings are loaded into AutoShade. To render the scene select one of the options from the **Display** menu.

CHAPTER 9

Autodesk 3D Studio

Introduction

3D Studio is an Autodesk software package designed for constructing, rendering and animating 3D model drawings. It will also render and animate 3D models constructed in AutoCAD, including those constructed with the aid of the Advanced Modelling Extension (AME).

Selection device

Selection of commands and the movement of details within the 3D editor display screen is carried out with the aid of a mouse. An alternative is a puck or stylus with a graphics tablet, perhaps used in conjunction with a mouse. It is possible to operate the programs from the keyboard with the cursor keys, but this will be found to be slow. Most commands can be called by entering letters or a combination of a key and a letter from the keyboard. In this book, it is assumed that all working is being performed with the aid of a mouse as the pointing device and that it has two buttons – left and right. To operate the mouse, buttons are clicked, i.e. they are pressed to achieve the required result. Note, however, that using the key alternatives for commands is often quicker than clicking on commands with the mouse.

Cursors

Several types of cursor will be seen, according to the operation being performed at the time. Some of these carry arrows showing the direction of action which can be taken with the aid of the cursor. The cursor varies according to the type of action required. Cursors are moved with the aid of the mouse and actions are initiated by clicking one or other of the mouse buttons.

Viewports

The program works with viewports (see page 66). Their number and size can be varied as will be seen later (Fig. 9.9). When the program is first loaded, the 3D Editor appears with four equally sized viewports as shown in Fig. 9.1. The active viewport, that in which the operator is working at any one time, is outlined by a heavy white line. Switching viewports is carried out by clicking in the required viewport.

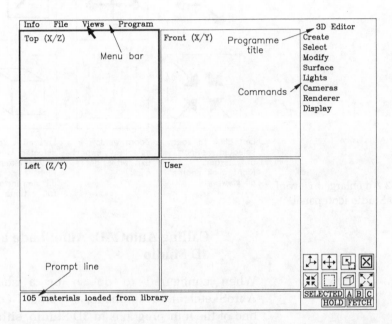

Fig. 9.1 The 3D Studio 3D Editor display screen

Dialogue and message boxes

Many operations performed in 3D Studio are associated with dialogue boxes, in which details can be entered from the keyboard, or message boxes displaying a message to which the operator can respond by clicking on buttons carrying words such as **OK**, **Create** and **Cancel**. Illustrations of a number of the boxes are included in this chapter.

Icon panel

A panel with eight icons will be seen at the bottom right-hand corner of the 3D Editor. Explanations of the responses to clicking on each of the icons are given in Fig. 9.2. In addition to the eight icon buttons, there are six buttons labelled **SELECTED**, **A**, **B**, **C**,

HOLD and **FETCH** below the icon buttons. In this book the purpose of these named and lettered buttons will not be explained, as they do not affect the simple explanations of renderings given here.

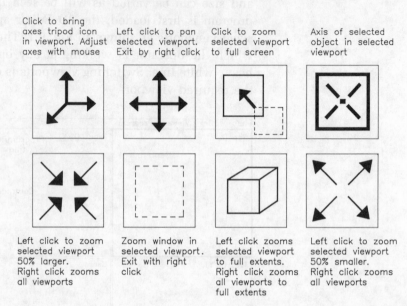

Click to bring axes tripod icon in viewport. Adjust axes with mouse

Left click to pan selected viewport. Exit by right click

Click to zoom selected viewport to full screen

Axis of selected object in selected viewport

Left click to zoom selected viewport 50% larger. Right click zooms all viewports

Zoom window in selected viewport. Exit with right click

Left click zooms selected viewport to full extents. Right click zooms all viewports to full extents

Left click to zoom selected viewport 50% smaller. Right click zooms all viewports

Fig. 9.2 An enlarged view of the 3D Studio icon panel

Calling AutoCAD, AutoShade and AutoSketch from 3D Studio

When configured to do so by a shell program, AutoCAD, AutoSketch and AutoShade, as well as DOS, can be called from any one of the four programs in 3D Studio, either by the selection of the name of the software from the **Program** pull-down menu, or by pressing a function key – F6 for AutoCAD, F7 for AutoSketch, F8 for AutoShade, F9 for DOS. To get back into 3D Studio from AutoCAD, select **Exit AutoCAD** (0) from the **Main Menu**. To get back to 3D Studio from AutoSketch select **Quit** from the **Files** pull-down menu. To get back into 3D Studio from AutoShade again select **Quit** from the **Files** pull-down menu. 3D Studio will accept 2D DXF files from AutoSketch.

Programs in 3D Studio

3D Studio contains four basic programs:

1. 2D Shaper for creating 2D shapes which can be formed into 3D models;
2. 3D Lofter for converting 2D shapes into 3D models (by **lofting**);

3. 3D Editor for editing 3D models created in the 2D Shaper and 3D Lofter programs and including those from filmroll and DXF files from AutoCAD; and

4. Keyframer for developing movement in 3D models.

It is not the purpose here to describe the full use and value of this software. To do so would require a whole book much larger than this one. In this book, it is only intended to show how the 3D Editor program of 3D Studio can be used for the rendering of some varied examples of filmroll files (*.flm files) of 3D models created in AutoCAD. It is hoped that this will be a useful introduction to this excellent software. These examples show only a fraction of the methods available for creating, developing and demonstrating the possibilities for rendering 3D models in a computer environment. No attempt is made in this chapter to describe the animating of models with the software.

Filenames and their extensions

Both DXF and filmroll files (files with the extension *.flm*) from AutoCAD can be loaded into 3D Studio. All the examples here involve loading filmroll files.

A number of types of file with the following filename extensions are used in 3D Studio as follows:

1. *.shp* files – 2D Shaper files;
2. *.lft* files – 3D Lofter files;
3. *.3ds* files – 3D Editor and Keyframer files;
4. *.mli* files – Materials files;
5. *.prj* files – Project files, with all components and settings in the same file;
6. *.dxf* files – Data Exchange Format files from AutoCAD;
7. *.flm* files – Filmroll files;
8. *.gif* files – For backgrounds to renderings;
9. *.cel* files – For backgrounds to renderings;
10. *.tga* files – Rendered image files;
11. *.tif* files – Bitmap files;
12. *.fli* files – Files from Autodesk Animator.

Of these – *.3ds, .cel, .flm, .gif, .prj* and *.tga* files will be referred to here.

Note about speed of rendering

Rendering takes time. The faster the speed of the CPU (Central Processing Unit) of the computer, the quicker will rendering take place. The fitting of a maths co-processor in the computer is essential. A suggested minimum PC (Personal Computer) equipment requirement for 3D Studio would be one fitted with an 80386 CPU chip, running at 20 MHz, with an 80387 math co-processor. However a computer fitted with an 80846 CPU chip running at 33 MHz, together with a Weitek co-processor, would give greatly improved speeds.

The 3D Editor of 3D Studio

The 3D Editor program of 3D Studio contains the following command sets:

1. Create: for the creation of 3D models from basic primitives; changing their shapes; development of complex models from the primitives created.
2. Select: for the selection of vertices, faces, elements and objects from 3D models.
3. Modify: for modifying vertices, edges, faces, elements and objects within 3D models.
4. Surface: for adding materials, smoothing and mapping surfaces, elements and objects in 3D models.
5. Lights: for adding and adjusting the intensity, colour and position of lights for illuminating the environment of 3D models.
6. Camera: for including and adjusting cameras in the 3D model environment.
7. Renderer: for setting and rendering a 3D model in its 3D Studio environment.
8. Display: for the displaying of various features connected with 3D models.

In this book there is no intention of dealing with either the Create or the Modify command sets from the 3D Editor program. Here, only those parts of the 3D Editor for adding materials, adding lights and cameras and for the rendering of 3D models from AutoCAD are mentioned.

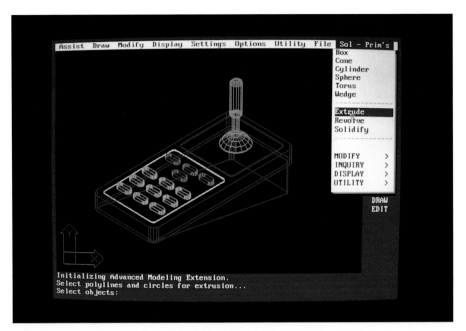

Plate 1   An AME model in the AutoCAD editor with the pull-down menu
Sol-Prims

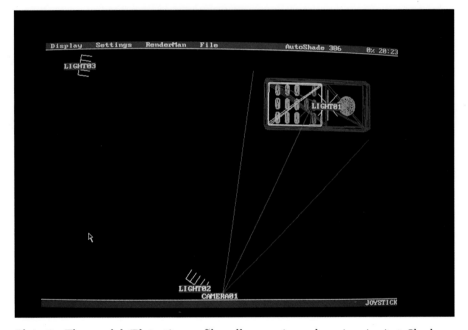

Plate 2   The model (Plate 1) as a filmroll scene in a plan view in AutoShade

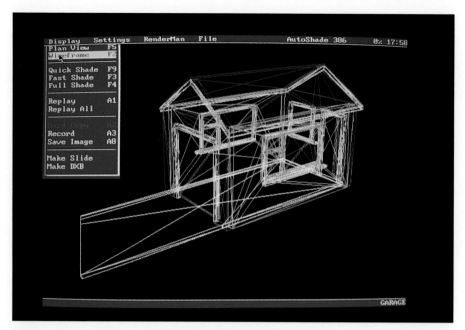

Plate 3 A wireframe view of an AME model in AutoShade with the **Display** pull-down menu

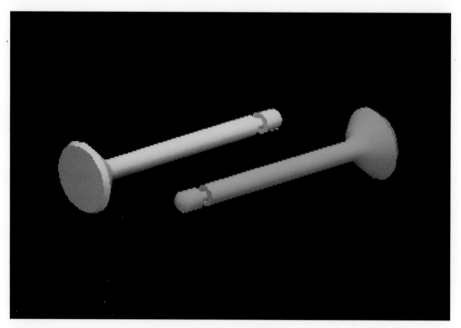

Plate 4 A full-shade rendering of a 3D **REVSURF** model of poppet valves in AutoShade

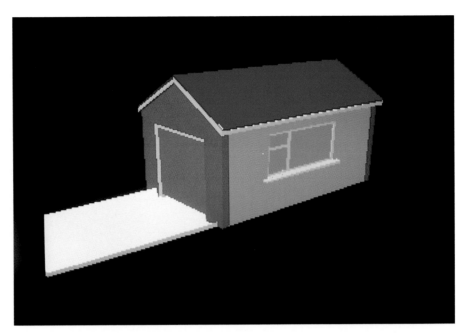

Plate 5   A full-shade rendering of an AME model of a garage in AutoShade

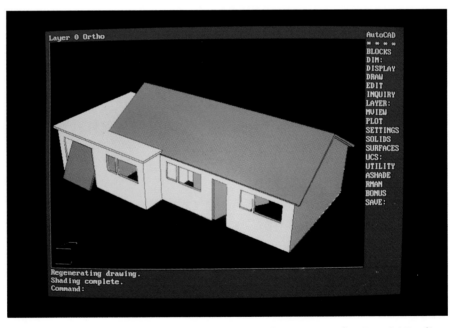

Plate 6   Figure 7.7 (page 124) after the action of **SHADE** in the AutoCAD editor

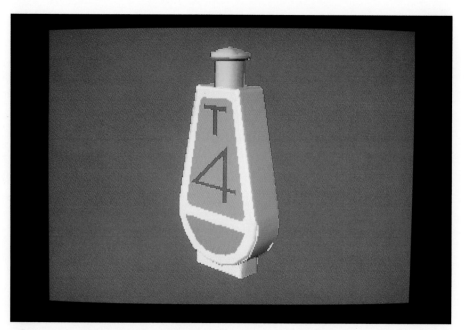

Plate 7　A full-shade rendering of an AME model of a dressing table bottle in AutoShade

Plate 8　The dressing table bottle (Plate 7) rendered in Autodesk 3D Studio

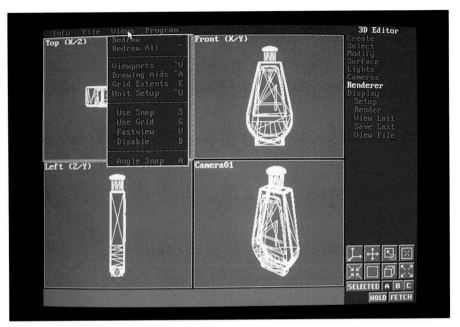

Plate 9 The dressing table bottle in the 3D Studio 3D Editor with the **Views** pull-down menu

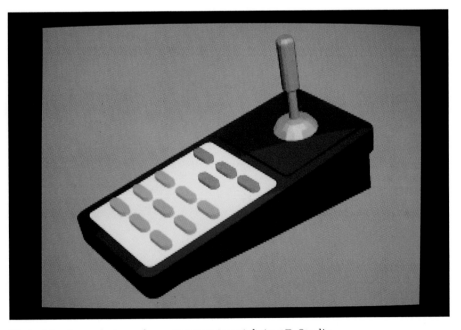

Plate 10 A rendering of a computer joystick in 3D Studio

Plate 11 A rendering of a garage in 3D Studio – compare with the same AME
model rendered in AutoShade (Plate 5)

Plate 12 A rendering of a stile in 3D Studio against a CEL background

Plate 13   A rendering of a silver vase in 3D Studio against a GIF background

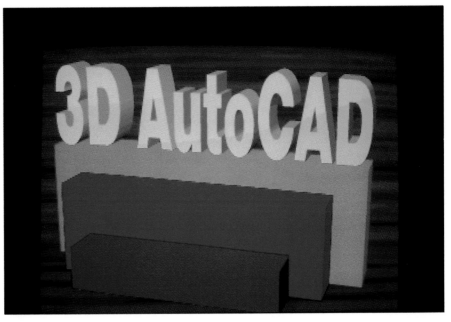

Plate 14   A model created and rendered in 3D Studio

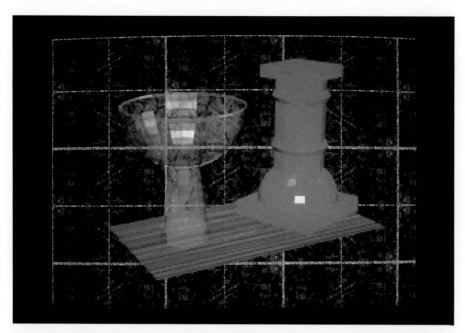

Plate 15 A glass bowl and its stand rendered in 3D Studio against a tiled
background

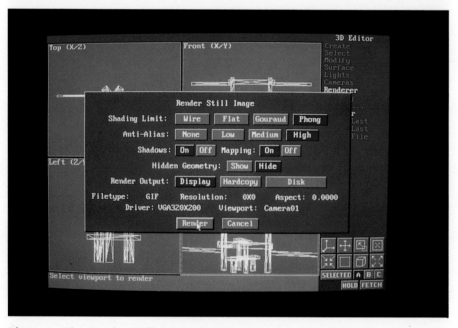

Plate 16 The **Render Still Image** dialogue box against the 3D editor screen of
3D Studio

Method of rendering a 3D model

Note that the methods for preparing a filmroll file (with the extensions .*flm*) is described in Chapter 8.

The method of producing a rendered image of a 3D model used in this book is as follows:

1. Click on the **File** pull-down menu from the **Menu** bar and load a filmroll file into the 3D display screen.
2. Make the views in each viewport a manageable size by clicking on the requisite zoom out or zoom in icon panel (bottom left corner of the 3D Editor display screen).
3. Add lights
   (a) Ambient
   (b) Omni. . . usually one, although several may be added;
   (c) Spot. . . several.
   Usually four lights in all will be sufficient.
   Adjust each light by moving in each viewport as necessary.
4. Add camera. Adjust by moving in each viewport as necessary.
5. Select **Viewports** from the **Views** pull-down menu and change the bottom right corner viewport to a camera one. This allows changes of camera position and lens lengths to be adjusted while the results of the changes can be seen in the camera viewport from the viewing position of the camera.
6. Select **Renderer/Render** to check lights in rendering.

Notes

1. Rendering inevitably takes some time, depending upon the complexity of the model and of the rendering.
2. Check, before assigning materials to see whether lights are OK as to position, colour and strength.
3. Adjust or delete lights as necessary.
4. When a scene has been rendered, pressing *Return* (on selection device or keyboard) brings back the 3D Editor display screen.
5. The sequences of clicking on 3D Studio commands and their option from in the command column of the 3D display screen in order to arrive at the command to be used are shown in the following way:

Surface/Material. . ./Choose

in the order of selection of the commands and options.
6. When clicking on a command name shown in the command

columns followed by three fullstops (. . .), a set of options will appear in the column.

7. Rendering to **W**ire takes less time than rendering **F**lat, which in turn takes less time than rendering **G**ourand. **P**hong usually produces better rendering, but takes the longest time. Thus to see the effects of lights and materials, a first trial rendering in **F**lat or **G**ourand may well save time. When satisfied that lights, materials and other details are satisfactory, then render in **P**hong.

Mapping, applying mapping coordinates and assigning materials

Material Properties

No matter what the colour of the object or element in the drawing originated in AutoCAD, the rendering material and its colour will be determined by the materials selection in 3D Studio. If a material is not assigned to an object, an element or a colour, the colour in the rendered image will be a neutral white (the default material), irrespective of its colour as set in AutoCAD.

If a material has only one of the properties **W**ire, **F**lat, **G**ourand or **P**hong, it need only be assigned to an object or an element in the 3D model being rendered. If a material has properties of **T**exture, **O**pacity or **B**ump, mapping coordinates will have to be applied to elements and objects in the 3D model. If mapping is not set and mapping coordinates applied for such materials, the material will not render.

In the 3D Studio Material Libraries *3ds.mli*, each material will have up to seven associated properties:

1. Column 1 (Shading Mode) – **W**(ire), **F**(lat), **G**(ourand), **P**(hong);
2. Column 2 – **X** if transparency is greater than 0;
3. Column 3 – **T** if a **T**exture map;
4. Column 4 – **O** if an **O**pacity map;
5. Column 5 – **R** if a **R**eflection map;
6. Column 6 – **B** if a **B**ump map;
7. Column 7 – 2 if two-sided.

Applying mapping and assigning materials

1. Materials which are mapped can only be assigned to elements or objects in a 3D model after mapping coordinates have been

applied. There are three types of mapping frames – planar, cylindrical and spherical. The mapping frame needs to be adjusted, moved, scaled, rotated, etc., in relation to the element or object in the 3D model. Then mapping coordinates must be applied. Only then can mapped materials be assigned to part of a 3D model.

2. Some mapped materials may have to be tiled. Tiling determines the size of the repeat of the pattern in the material selected when a Mapped material is used. Tiling must be set (e.g. 4 × 4 for a smaller repeat pattern than the 1 × 1 repeat set with the material). Tiling must be set before a material can be assigned.

3. Finally, choose a material and assign it to the object or element which has had mapping coordinates applied.

The process of mapping and assigning materials follows a sequence of commands and options such as:

1.   **3D Editor/Surface/Mapping. . ./Type**
      Surface/Mapping. . ./Type/Cylindrical
      Surface/Mapping. . ./Adjust/Move
      Surface/Mapping. . ./Adjust/Scale
      Surface/Mapping. . ./Adjust/Height
      Surface/Mapping. . ./Adjust/Tiling
      Surface/Mapping. . ./Apply/Object

2.   **3D Editor/Surface/Material. . ./Choose**
      Material. . ./Assign/By Name
      Material. . ./Assign/Object

3.   **3D Editor/Rendering/Setup. . ./Background**
      Rendering/Render

Those materials which are not **B**ump, **O**pacity, **R**eflection or **T**exture maps do not need to have mapping coordinates applied to the elements, faces or objects required to carry the materials. The following is an example of applying mapping and assigning a material which is a **B**ump map:

1. **Lights/Ambient**: accept the default values of 30/30/30 – a brighter general overall lighting would tend to affect other lighting and cause less sharpness of lighting effects.

2. **Lights/Omni. . ./Create**: accept values of 100/100/100.

3. **Lights/Omni. . ./Move**: move to overhead in the top viewport.

4. **Lights/Spot. . ./Create**: accept values of 100/100/100.

5. **Lights/Spot. . ./Move**: move to better position.

6. **Lights/Spot. . ./Create**: repeat with a second spot light, but with values of 60/60/60.

7. **Cameras/Create**: in top viewport, accept 50 mm.
8. **Cameras/Move**: move to good position.
9. **Views pull-down/Viewports**: make User Viewport the Camera Viewport.
10. **Cameras/Move**: adjust camera to obtain good view in camera Viewport.
11. **Display/Hide. . ./Lights**
12. **Display/Hide. . ./Cameras**
13. **Views (pull-down)/Redraw All**
14. Right click on **Zoom Extents** to zoom all viewports to extents.
15. **Surface/Mapping. . ./Adjust/Move**
16. **Surface/Mapping. . ./Aspect/Height**: adjust and aspect of mapping.
17. **Surface/Mapping. . ./Apply. . ./Object**: apply mapping to required objects by colour/number.
18. **Surface/Material. . ./Choose**: choose from library that appears.
19. **Surface/Material. . ./Assign. . ./By Name**: assign to colour/number.

Mapping coordinates and materials can be applied and/or assigned to an object by colour coding (using the colour coding 01 to 07 – red to white) or to a face or to an element in a 3D model by clicking on the element.

Examples of rendering AutoCAD filmrolls

Eight examples of 3D Studio renderings are described below. A variety of types of model are illustrated by these examples. They include a number of different materials, some of which have been mapped, and a variety of backgrounds. The results of the renderings are shown in the colour plates (between pages 148 and 149). Each was rendered with the Shading Limit set to **P**hong and with Anti-Alias set to High. Before setting these, colours, lights, background and materials were checked by first rendering with the shading limit set to **F**lat and anti-alias set to Low. This enabled faster rendering than with **P**hong shading and high anti-alias. When satisfied a final rendering to **P**hong and High was run.

The examples are:

1. A bevel gear – an AutoCAD **RULESURF** model.
   Filmroll – *bevgear.flm*.   A detailed description of the sequence for producing this rendering is included below.
2. Two poppet valves – AutoCAD **REVSURF** model.
   Filmroll – *valves.flm*.

3. A glass bowl and its stand. AutoCAD **REVSURF** models.
    Filmroll – *revsurf.flm*.
4. A computer game joystick – AutoCAD AME model.
    Filmroll – *joystick.flm*.
5. A silver vase. An AutoCAD **REVSURF** model.
    Filmroll – *vase.flm.*.
6. A brick garage – an AutoCAD AME solid model.
    Filmroll – *garage.flm*.
7. A dressing table bottle – AutoCAD AME solid model.
    Filmroll – *bottle.flm*.
8. A stile set in a background – AutoCAD AME solid model.
    Filmroll – *stile.flm*.

An example of rendering in the 3D Editor of 3D Studio

Introduction

1. As each of the actions described in the following procedures is
    carried out, prompts will appear at the prompt line in the 3D
    Editor display screen. These prompts describe the action to be
    taken by the operator to achieve the desired effects.
2. The screen cursor (its position on the screen under the control
    of the mouse movements) changes shape according to the type
    of command being followed at the time.
3. Dialogue and message boxes appear to assist the operator from
    time to time. Each of these is shown by an illustration.
4. Selection of commands are shown as, for example:

    Lights/Omni. . ./Create

    To follow this instruction, first click on **Lights** in the Command
    column, then when the sub-menu appears, click on **Omni. . .**,
    followed by clicking on **Create**.
5. All of the model bevgear was constructed in AutoCAD in the
    colour 07 (white). In 3D Studio this becomes the **Object
    Color07**.

The procedure for rendering the bevel gear model

1. At the C:> DOS prompt, enter *3Ds* from keyboard. The 3Ds
    display screen appears showing the 3D Editor screen (Fig.
    9.1).

2. (a) Click on **File** (Menu bar). Dialogue box (Fig. 9.3);
    (b) Click on **Load**;
    (c) Click on ***.FLM**;
    (d) Click on **CHAP09**;
    (e) Click on **BEVGEAR.FLM**;
    (f) Click on **OK**. Dialogue box disappears and different views of the model appear in each of the viewports (Fig. 9.4).

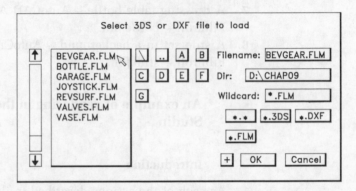

Fig. 9.3 The **3DS** or **DXF** file to load dialogue box

3. **Lights/Ambient. . . .** Dialogue box (Fig. 9.5). Click on **OK** to accept R/G/B = 30/30/30.
4. Right click twice on **Zoom** smaller icon in icon display panel to reduce model in viewports 100% smaller.
5. **Lights/Omni. . ./Create**. Dialogue box (Fig. 9.6):
    (a) Click in **Front** viewport to position the Omni light;
    (b) Click on **OK** to accept R/G/B = 100/100/100;
    (c) **Lights/Omni. . ./Move**;
    (d) Click in **Front** viewport and move Omni light.
6. **Lights/Spot. . ./Create**:
    (a) Click in **Top** viewport to position the spotlight;
    (b) Click to position the spotlight target;
    (c) Dialogue box (Fig. 9.7);
    (d) Click on **Create** to accept R/G/B = 100/100/100 and **Hotspot** and **Falloff** angles = 45.
7. **Lights/Spot. . ./Move**. Move Spotlight in **Front** and **Left** viewports to acceptable position.
8. Repeat operations 6 and 7 to add two further spotlights:
    (a) One with R/G/B = 50/50/50; and
    (b) Another with R/G/B = 50/65/85 – a light blue.
    (c) Move the second to behind and below the model.
9. **Cameras/Create**
    (a) Place a camera and the camera's target near the first

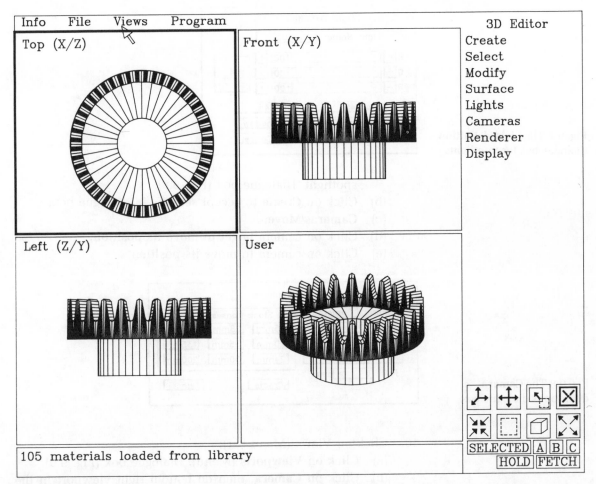

Fig. 9.4 The file
BEVGEAR.FLM loaded into
the 3D Editor

Fig. 9.5 The **Ambient light
definition** dialogue box

Fig. 9.6 The **Light definition**
dialogue box for **O**mni lights

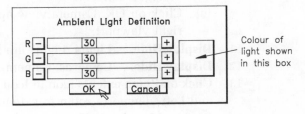

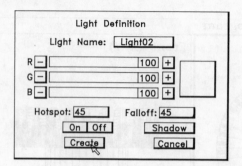

Fig. 9.7 The **Light definition** dialogue box for **Spotlights**

spotlight. Dialogue box (Fig. 9.8);
(b)   Click on **Create** to accept settings in dialogue box;
(c)   **Cameras/Move**;
(d)   Click on camera target to move its position;
(e)   Click on camera to move its position.

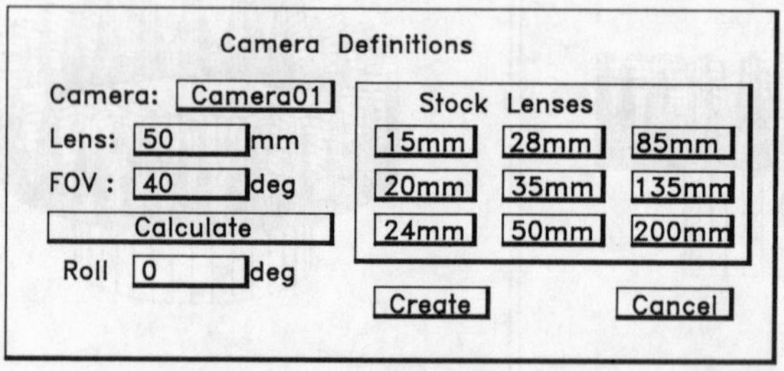

Fig. 9.8 The **Camera definitions** dialogue box

10.   Click on **Views** (Menu bar):
      (a)   Click on **Viewports** (Menu). Dialogue box (Fig. 9.9);
      (b)   Click on **Camera**, then on bottom right viewport in the dialogue box;
      (c)   Click on **OK**. Camera view appears in 3D Editor bottom right viewport.
11.   **Display/Hide. . ./Lights**. Lights are hidden.
12.   **Display/Hide. . ./Cameras**. Camera is hidden.
13.   Click on **Zoom extents** icon in Icon panel. Views in **Top**, **Front** and **Left** viewports zoom to extents.
14.   **Surface/Mapping. . ./Type. . ./Cylindrical**.
15.   **Surface/Mapping. . ./Adjust. . ./Move**   and   **Surface/Mapping. . ./Adjust. . ./Scale** – adjust mapping cylinder to fit around model.
16.   **Surface/Mapping. . ./Aspect. . ./Height** – adjust mapping cylinder for height.
17.   **Surface/Mapping. . ./Apply. . ./Object**:
      (a)   Click on the model in the **Front** viewport;

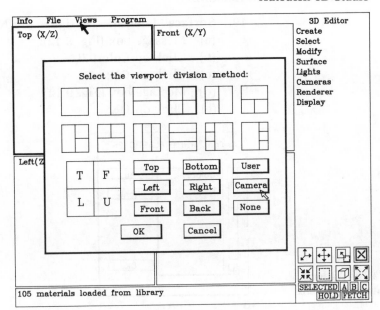

Fig. 9.9 The dialogue box for viewports division

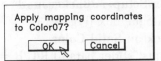

Fig. 9.10 The **Mapping coordinates** message box

    (b)   Message box (Fig. 9.10);

    (c)   Click on **OK**.

18.   **Surface/Material. . ./Choose**:

    (a)   Dialogue box (Fig. 9.11);

    (b)   Click on **WHITE PLASTIC 2S   P   2**;

    (c)   Click on **OK**.

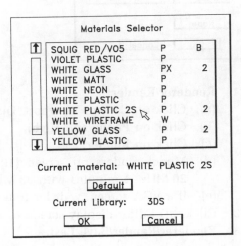

Fig. 9.11 The **Materials selector** dialogue box

19. **Surface/Material. . ./Assign. . ./By Name**:
    (a) Message box (Fig. 9.12);
    (b) Click on **Color07**;
    (c) Click on **OK**;
    (d) Message box (Fig. 9.12);
    (e) Click on **OK**.

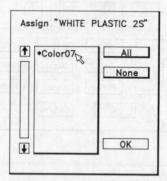

Fig. 9.12 The **Assign materials** dialogue box

20. **Renderer/Setup. . ./Background**:
    (a) Dialogue box (Fig. 9.13);
    (b) Click on **Solid Color**;
    (c) Adjust slider bars to R/G/B = 170/100/190 (magenta);
    (d) Click on **OK**.

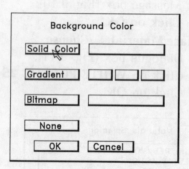

Fig. 9.13 The **Background color** dialogue box

21. **Renderer/Render**:
    (a) Click on Camera Viewport. Dialogue box (Fig. 9.14);
    (b) Click on **Phong** and **High**;
    (c) Click on **Render**;
    (d) Model renders on screen (10 minutes with VGA and 20 MHz, 4 minutes with 33 Mhz);
    (e) If a VGA screen, wait for true colours to re-render.
22. Click. 3D Editor display screen re-appears.
23. **Renderer/Render/Save Last**:

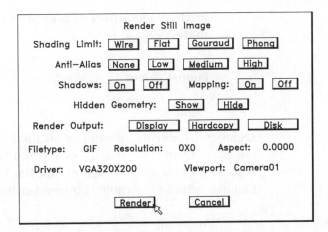

Fig. 9.14 The **Render still image** dialogue box

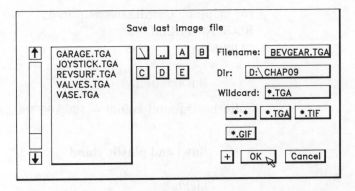

Fig. 9.15 The **Save last image file** dialogue box

(a) Dialogue box (Fig. 9.15);

(b) Enter **BEVGEAR.TGA** in **Filename:** box;

(c) Click on **OK**. File is saved as *BEVGEAR.TGA*.

24. To see the rendered model again,

Renderer/Render/View Last

25. Save the drawing and rendering details as *bevgear.prj* by clicking on the **Files** menu, then on **Save Project** in that menu and entering the name *BEVGEAR* at the **Filename** box. Saving as a Project file with the extension *.prj* saves all settings such as the lighting, cameras, materials and background details with the model drawing.

Further examples of mapping and assigning materials

Poppet valves

Lights

Light01:   Ambient: default of 30/30/30
Light02:   Omni: default of 100/100/100
Light03:   Spot: default of 100/100/100
Light04:   Spot: 80/80/80 targeted from below and behind

Materials

No mapping coordinates required.
BLUE METALLIC P
COPPER   P

Background

Solid background colour – 160/160/160 (grey).

Bowl and plastic stand

Lights

Light01:   Ambient: default of 30/30/30
Light02:   Omni: default of 100/100/100
Light03:   Spot: 50/50/50
Light04:   Spot: 40/40/40 targeted below and behind

Materials

The two-sided material Green Glass and the texture map Palm Tree Trunk both needed mapping coordinates applied. Mapping coordinates were applied to the bowl with cylindrical type and to the mat on which the objects stand with a Planar type.

GREEN GLASS   PX 2
PALM TREE TRUNK P T B
RED PLASTIC   P

Background

Bitmap: *Brownmarb.cel*

Joystick

Lights

Light01: Ambient: default of 30/30/30
Light02: Omni: default of 100/100/100
Light03: Spot: 50/50/50
Light04: Spot: 40/40/40 targeted below and behind

Materials

No mapping was required for this rendering.

DARK BROWN MATTE P
COPPER   P
RED PLASTIC   P
GREEN PLASTIC   P
YELLOW PLASTIC   P

Background

Solid background colour – 140/140/140 (Grey)

The results of the rendering of this example are shown in Plate 10.

Vase

Lights

Light01: Ambient: default of 30/30/30
Light02: Omni: default of 100/100/100
Light03: Spot: default of 100/100/100
Light04: Spot: default of 100/100/100

Material

The Reflection map Chrome Gifmap was assigned to the vase (object colour02) after mapping coordinates had been applied through a cylindrical type of mapping.

Background

Bitmap *Clouds.cel*

The results of the rendering of this example are shown in Plate 13.

Brick garage

Lights

Light01:	Ambient:	default of 30/30/30
Light02:	Omni:	default of 100/100/100
Light03:	Spot:	default of 100/100/100
Light04:	Spot:	default of 100/100/100
Light05:	Spot:	default of 100/100/100

Materials

		Column							
		1	2	3	4	5	6	7	
Color01:	Red Plastic:	P							Doors
Color02:	White Plastic:	P							Woodwork
Color03:	Concrete Tile:	G		T					Floor
Color04:	Bumpy Brownbrick:	P		T			B		Front wall
Color05:	Bumpy Brownbrick:	P		T			B		Side walls
Color06:	Dark Wood Inlay:	P		T					Roof
Color07:	Glass:	P	X					2	Windows

In this example it will be seen that the walls, roof and windows had to have mapping coordinates applied before the materials could be assigned. In addition, the tiling factor was set to 4 × 4 for all the assigned mapping coordinates.

Background

Solid background colour – 150/150/150 (grey)

The results of the rendering of this example are shown in Plate 11.

Dressing table bottle

Lights

Light01:	Ambient:	default of 30/30/30
Light02:	Omni:	65/80/65
Light03:	Spot:	default of 100/100/100
Light04:	Spot:	60/75/60

Materials		Column							
		1	2	3	4	5	6	7	
Color01	Red Plastic	P							Letters on label
Color02	Gold	P							Cap
Color03	Aqua Bumpfli 61F	P					B		Label
Color07	Green Glass	P	X					2	Bottle body

From the above it will be seen that the Green Glass and Label materials had mapping coordinates applied before the materials could be assigned.

Background

Solid background colour – 140/70/120

The results of the rendering of this example are shown in Plate 8.

CHAPTER 10

Examples of 3D models

Introduction

Nine examples of a variety of 3D models drawn in AutoCAD together with one created in Autodesk 3D Studio are given in this chapter. These 10 show a variety of methods of constructing, either with the AutoCAD **SURFACE** command systems or with the Advanced Modelling Extension. 3D Studio renderings of two of the examples are shown in colour plates (Plates 12 and 14).

Example 1 – a stile

A **VPOINT** parallel projection view of the model is given in Fig. 10.1. The model was constructed with the aid of the two AME commands **SOLBOX** and **SOLCYL**. All parts of the construction were acted upon by **SOLUNION** and **SOLMESH** before being transferred to 3D Studio via a filmroll file for rendering.

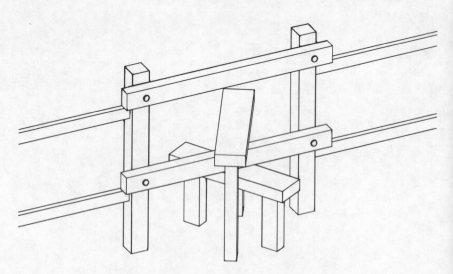

Fig. 10.1 Example 1 – a stile

The 3D Studio rendering parameters were as follows:

Lighting

Light01:   Ambient: default of 30/30/30
Light02:   Omni: default of 100/100/100
Light03:   Spot: default of 100/100/100

Materials

Color01   Blue Metallic   P
Color07   Brown Matte   P

Background

VALLEY_L.TGA

The results of the rendering are shown in Plate 12.

Example 2 – a tiled table

Figure 10.2 is a plot of a **DVIEW** (**Di**stance) perspective projection of the model. The model was constructed in AutoCAD with the aid of AME. The table frame consists of a number of **SOLBOX**es, with the outer corners of the legs **SOLFILL**ed. The frame **SOLBOX**es were acted upon by **SOLUNION** to form a single Boolean solid model. A single tile was constructed with **SOLBOX** and a pattern added on its top surface with **PLINE**s of 1 unit thickness. The

Fig. 10.2 Example 2 – a tiled table

single tile was then **COPY**ed to obtain the 15 tiles for the table top. In order to keep the tiles as separate units, they were not acted upon by **SOLUNION**. The whole model was given surface meshes with **SOLMESH**, before **DVIEW** was called.

Example 3 – a machine part

Figure 10.3 is a four viewport plot of an AME model with dimensions added to the orthographic views in three of the viewports. The model was constructed from **SOLBOX**es, with **SOLFILL**s and **SOLCYL**s. The holes in the base were created by using **SOLSUB** to subtract **SOLCYL**s from the base. Three UCS systems were used – ***WORLD*** – one viewing from the front (UCS **FRONT**) and another viewing from the end (UCS **END**). The four views were positioned with the aid of **VPOINT**, after turning UCS **FOLLOW** off in each viewport. Note that when adding dimensions to AME models in orthographic views, **OSNAP**s cannot be used – if used there is no surety that the snapping will be at the intended position.

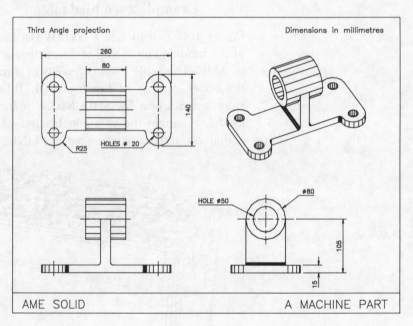

Fig. 10.3 Example 3 – a machine part

Example 4 – a support bracket

Figure 10.4 is a plot of the three-viewport screen of this AME model. The model was constructed by following the sequence:

1. **UCSFOLLOW ON** (1);
2. **UCS** 3point – UCS surface as viewed from the front;
3. **UCS** – save as **FRONT**;
4. **ARC** – draw double arc of part A;
5. **PLINE** – add plines to form the flat end piece of part A. Join the right-hand ends of the arcs with a pline;
6. **PEDIT** – join plines and arcs into a continuous pline;
7. **SOLEXTRUDE** – extrude the pline to its required height with angle to Z at 0;
8. In a similar manner form the web – i.e. an AME extrusion from a pline outline;
9. **UCS** – *WORLD*;
10. **SOLMOVE** – move the two extrusions to suitable positions;
11. In a similar manner form the front open end and the 'shelf' of the bracket – i.e. AME extrusions from pline outlines;
12. **SOLCYL** – two cylinders for the bolt holes;
13. **UCS** – restore **FRONT** – check that the parts of the model are positioned correctly in relation to each other. If not, use **SOLMOVE** to reposition them;
14. **SOLSUB** – subtract the two bolt holes from extrusion A;
15. **SOLUNION** – all parts;
16. **SOLMESH**;
17. **TILEMODE** – **ON** (0);
18. **LIMITS** – set **P**aper **S**pace limits to 420,300;
19. **ZOOM** – **All**;
20. **LAYER** – make a new layer **VIEWPORT**, Colour 2 (Yellow);
21. **MVIEW** – 3; Top; Fit;

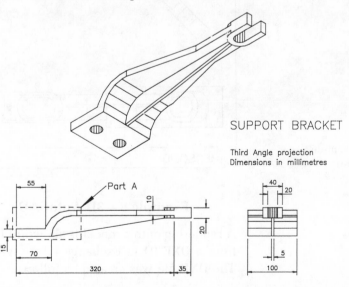

SUPPORT BRACKET

Third Angle projection
Dimensions in millimetres

Fig. 10.4 Example 4 – a support bracket

22. **MSPACE** – **UCSFOLLOW OFF** (0) in each viewport in turn;
23. **VPOINT** – Top-1,−1.5,−1; Bottom left 0,−1,0; Bottom right 1,0,0;
24. **ZOOM** – 1 in each viewport in turn;
25. **MOVE** – move viewports to suitable positions;
26. **LAYER** – set layer 0;
27. **MVIEW** – Hideplot – **ON** – turn on each viewport in turn;
28. **LAYER** – turn layer **VIEWPORT OFF**.

Example 5 – a machine part

Figure 10.5 is a four-viewport plot of this model. It has been constructed from **SOLBOX**es, **SOLCYL**s and **SOLEXT**rusions, on a number of different UCS systems. **SOLSUB**, **SOLUNION** and **SOLMESH** were called to complete the model. The methods of placing the model in four viewports followed the routines given with Example 4 above. Finally, the model was acted upon by **SOLPROF** and the layers 0 and 1-PH-2 turned off to produce profile only views.

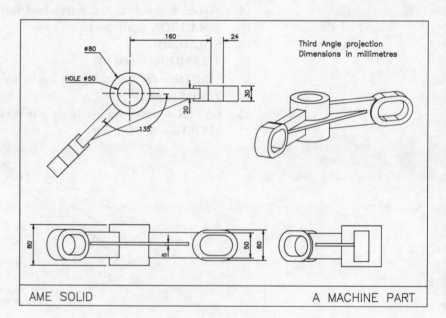

Fig. 10.5 Example 5 – a machine part

Example 6 – 3D AutoCAD

A rendering of this model is shown in Plate 14. Figure 10.6 is a plot from a **DXF** (Data Exchange File) saved from a 3D Studio model. The **DXF** file was created as follows:

1. Outlines of the four parts of the model were drawn in the 2D Shaper program of 3D Studio;
2. The outlines were 'lofted' to give them thickness in the 3D Lofter program of 3D Studio;
3. Lights, camera, materials and rendering background were added in the 3D Editor program of 3D Studio;
4. The views of the model in the 3D Editor of 3D Studio were saved as:
   (a) A project file (extension .*prj*), which includes all details of the model, its lights, camera, materials and rendering background;
   (b) A Data Exchange File (extension .*dxf*);
5. The **DXF** file was loaded into AutoCAD.

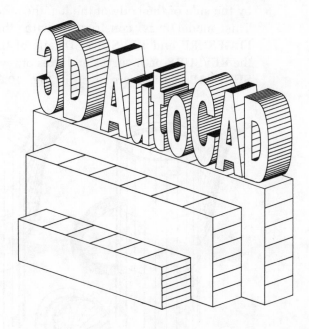

Fig. 10.6 Example 6 – a model created in Autodesk 3D Studio

Details of lighting, camera, materials and rendering background for this model

Lighting

Light01:	Ambient:	default of 30/30/30
Light02:	Omni:	default of 100/100/100
Light03:	Spot:	default of 100/100/100
Light04:	Spot:	60/60/60

Materials – assigned to named objects

Letters:	Gold	P
Back:	Red Plastic	P
Middle:	Blue Plastic 100	P
Front:	Green Matte	P

Rendering background

TREETRUNK.CEL

Example 7 – a coffee jug

Figure 10.7 shows two views of this model, one with the lid lying by the side of the body of the jug, the second with the lid in place. This model was constructed with the **SURFACE** commands **EDGESURF** and **REVSURF**. Details of the **EDGESURF** edges and the **REVSURF** path curves and axes of revolution, together with the **SURFTAB** settings, are given in Figs 10.8 and 10.9.

Fig. 10.7 Example 7 – two views of a coffee jug

Example 8 – a door handle

Figure 10.10 is a **SOLPROF** view of this model. Constructed from **SOLBOX**es, **SOLCYL**s, **SOLCONE**s, with edges of the backplate **SOLFILL**eted. The handle is an AME extrusion from a pline outline. The given plot is a profile only view obtained by calling SOLPROF. Layers 0 and 1-PH-2 have been turned off.

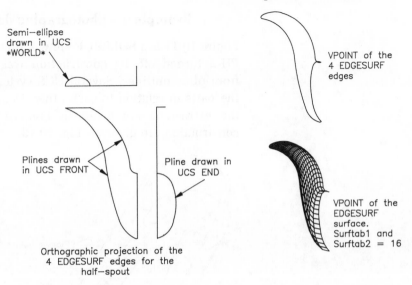

Semi—ellipse drawn in UCS *WORLD*

VPOINT of the 4 EDGESURF edges

Plines drawn in UCS FRONT

Pline drawn in UCS END

VPOINT of the EDGESURF surface. Surftab1 and Surftab2 = 16

Orthographic projection of the 4 EDGESURF edges for the half—spout

Fig. 10.8 Example 7 – Constructions for the spout

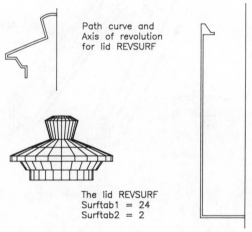

Path curve and Axis of revolution for lid REVSURF

Path curve and Axis of revolution for body REVSURF

The lid REVSURF
Surftab1 = 24
Surftab2 = 2

Fig. 10.9 Example 7 – Constructions for the body and lid

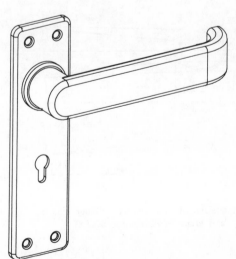

Fig. 10.10 Example 8 – a door handle

Example 9 – photographic developing tongs

Figure 10.11 is a **SOLPROF** view of this model, with layers 0 and 1-PH-2 turned off. Its construction was based on **SOLEXT**rusions from pline outlines. Several UCS systems were formed to position the parts in relation to each other. Details of the pline outlines for the extrusions are given in Fig. 10.12. Further details of the construction are given in Fig. 10.13.

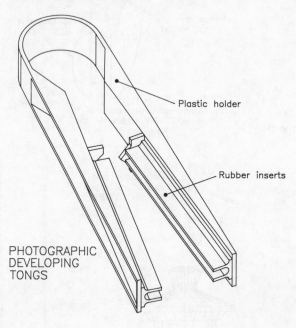

Fig. 10.11 Example 9 – photographic developing tongs

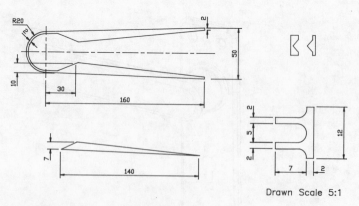

Fig. 10.12 Example 9 – pline outlines for the extrusions

Dimensions of body, inserts, rubber inserts and stops – PLINEs for SOLEXT

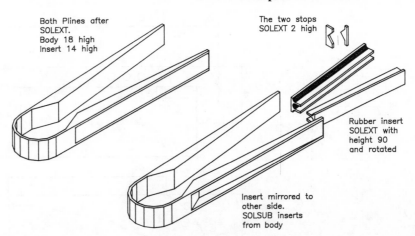

Both Plines after
SOLEXT.
Body 18 high
Insert 14 high

The two stops
SOLEXT 2 high

Rubber insert
SOLEXT with
height 90
and rotated

Insert mirrored to
other side.
SOLSUB inserts
from body

Fig. 10.13 Example 9 –
stages in creating the solids

Example 10 – pipe grips

Figure 10.14 is a **SOLPROF** view of an exploded projection of this
model. Details of the pline outlines from which the **SOLEXT**rusions
were developed are given in Fig. 10.15. When these extrusions had
been created, **SOLCYL**s were **SOLSUB**bed from both parts. Two
extrusions were needed for the body together with an extrusion
created from a double arc (constructed in UCS **END**). The given plot
is a profile only one after calling **SOLPROF** and turning layers 0
and 1-PH-2 off.

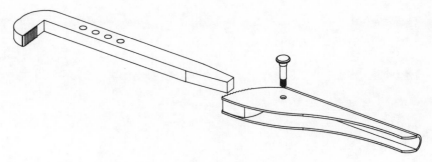

Fig. 10.14 Example 10 – pipe
wrench

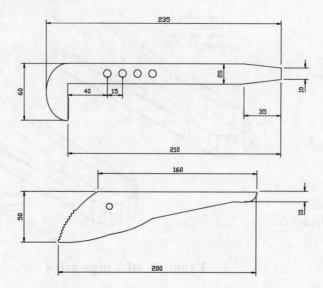

Fig. 10.15 Example 10 –
pline outlines for extrusions

Appendix
Notes on AutoCAD Release 12

AutoCAD Release 12 is a major new release containing many additions and enhancements over earlier releases of the software. The following notes are therefore not comprehensive, but are intended to show those additions and enhancements contained in the Release 12 package, which are of interest to readers of this book. The more advanced enhancements included in Release 12 are not shown below.

1. The most important feature of Release 12 in relation to the contents of this book is that the core of Release 11 remains in Release 12.
2. Release 12 works in a dialogue box system, mainly in a windows based environment.
3. Pull-down menus can be cascaded on screen.
4. It has all the usual GUI (Graphical User Interface) window type features:
   (a) Mouse selection;
   (b) Mouse down and drag;
   (c) Mouse double-click to accept;
   (d) Active icons;
   (e) Movable dialogue boxes in windows;
   (f) Scrolling;
   (g) 3D appearance of buttons;
   (h) Pop-up lists.
5. Release 12 is fully compatible with Release 11.
6. Normally, the rule for the loading of AutoCAD drawing files is that any drawing from an earlier release can be loaded into a later release. However, with Release 12, Release 12 drawing files can be loaded into Release 11 and vice versa.
7. When AutoCAD is loaded, the **Main menu** common to earlier Releases does not appear. Instead, the AutoCAD goes straight into the drawing editor. Existing drawing files can be selected

from a pull-down menu, with a dialogue box containing file-names.

8. Release 12 is faster in operation than earlier releases.
9. It has some new hatching enhancements.
10. Hatching is by pointing into an enclosed area to be hatched rather than by selecting entities around an area to be hatched.
11. It has some new dimensioning enhancements.
12. It has some new system variables.
13. 3D array, 3D mirror, 3D rotate and 3D align are available.
14. Hidden lines in 3D models can be removed faster – by placing them on a new layer.
15. Non-plottable construction lines are available.
16. It has an Autosave system – which can be set for time before Autosave acts.
17. An AutoCAD for the MS-DOS Windows environment is available.
18. AutoShade is included as part of AutoCAD Release 12.

Index